Everyman's Guide to Ecological Living

S0-CFW-588

This is the symbol of ecology, which represents a fusion of the letters "e" and "o". The "e" represents our environment, earth. The "o" stands for the oneness of our house ("oikos") and the organisms which inhabit it.

Original artwork by Judy Daniel

This book is printed on paper made from paper. Recycled paper saves trees.

Santa Barbara Underseas Foundation

The Santa Barbara Underseas Foundation is proud of the part it played in the production of this book. We are a non-profit, tax-exempt organization, founded in 1968, and dedicated to educating the general public about oceanography and marine life as well as utilizing our marine environment as a laboratory for geological and ecological studies. Special emphasis is placed on understanding and solving our environmental crises.

Continuing our role in the conservation movement, the Foundation is sponsoring an occasional publication entitled "Everyman's Way," designed to keep you informed on ecological problems and the efforts being made to solve them.

An annual membership rate entitles you to receive a FREE subscription to "Everyman's Way" and at the same time provides support for our programs.

Contributing	$10.00	Associate Fellow	$50.00
Family	15.00	Educational Fellow	100.00
Associate	25.00	Institutional	300.00

Mail your tax deductible fee and application to:

Santa Barbara Underseas Foundation
Box 4815
Santa Barbara, Calif. 93103

Everyman's Guide to Ecological Living

GREG M. CAILLIET

PAULETTE Y. SETZER

MILTON S. LOVE

The Macmillan Company, *New York*
Collier-Macmillan Limited, *London*

Copyright © 1971, The Santa Barbara
Underseas Foundation, Inc., P.O. Box 4815
Santa Barbara, California 93103

Printed in the United States of America

All rights reserved. No part of this book may
be reproduced or transmitted in any form or
by any means, electronic or mechanical, including photocopying, recording, or any
information storage and retrieval system,
without permission in writing from the
Publisher.

The Macmillan Company
866 Third Avenue, New York,
New York 10022
Collier-Macmillan Canada, Ltd.,
Toronto, Ontario

Library of Congress catalog card number:
79–151240

Second Printing, 1971

"B.C." cartoons by permission of John Hart
and Field Enterprises, Inc.

Editorial cartoons by Interlandi copyright *Los
Angeles Times*. Reprinted with permission.

"Pogo" cartoon © 1970 Walt Kelly. Courtesy
of Publishers-Hall Syndicate.

Contents

FOREWORD   vii

ACKNOWLEDGMENTS   viii

INTRODUCTION   1

GENERAL RULES TO LIVE BY   4

RESOURCES TO BE CONSERVED   7

Packaging Materials   7
   Aluminum and Tin Cans   7
   Glass Bottles and Jars   10
   Plastics   14
   Wax-Cardboard Containers   17
   Shopping Bags   18
Wood and Paper Products   19
   Wood   19
   Newspapers   21
   Magazines and Telephone Books   24
   Books   25
   Stationery, Cards, and Wrapping   26
   Advertising   28
   Miscellaneous Paper Products   29
Solid Waste Disposal   30
   Recycling Centers   31
   Municipal Operations   34
Petroleum Products   36
   Transportation   36
   Power Generation and Use   39

Air 41
Water 45
   Conservation of Water 45
   Water Quality and Sewage Treatment 48
Metals 52
Food 53
Food Scraps 57
   Homemade Soap recipe 58
   Composting 59
Endangered Wildlife 61
Land 64

CONSUMER POWER 70
POLLUTANTS 73
Pesticides 73
Herbicides 84
Cleansers 85
Metallic Toxins 92
   Lead 92
   Mercury 94

POLITICAL ACTION 96
POPULATION 100
WILL TECHNOLOGY SAVE US? 105
RECOMMENDED INFORMATION AND ACTION SOURCES 106
Books 106
Periodicals 110
Organizations 111

LITERATURE CITED 115

Foreword

On January 28, 1969, the nation had its attention focused upon Santa Barbara, California. Because of a runaway oil well offshore, the city that had been a symbol of California's natural beauty became overnight a symbol of pollution. On the first anniversary of that disaster, a conference on environmental rights was held in Santa Barbara. This conference pointed out the dire need for action, but left many with the question, "What can I, as an individual, do?" The authors of this handbook have attempted to answer this important and urgent question, basing a large part of this edition on the tremendous volume of suggestions and questions generated by previous smaller editions distributed locally.

It may well be asked why the Santa Barbara Underseas Foundation has sponsored this publication. The SBUF is devoted to the primary causes of environmental education. Because of our backgrounds, education, interests, and location, we have focused on the oceans. However, we have done this with the recognition that the ocean is only a part of the whole, and unless we can conserve this whole, all of its fractions, including the seas, will be irreparably damaged.

Richard S. Lee, President
Santa Barbara Underseas Foundation

Greg M. Cailliet
Paulette Y. Setzer
Milton S. Love

Acknowledgments

This manual is a product of evolution through three earlier editions. Many people have aided us with ideas, encouragement, and services. Their energetic suggestions and helpful generosity have enabled us to improve the quality of successive editions.

Ideas and information were contributed by Mer Cailliet, James Case, Lou and DeDe Chauvin, Pete Craig, Jerry and Joy Croteau, Judy Daniel, William Denneen, Floyd and Donna DeWitt, Larry Friesen, Sheelagh Fuzessery, Henry Genthe, Peter Lorber, Ferren MacIntyre, Patrick McKeon, Mary Menzel, Sue Mogee, Raphael and Jan Payne, Jack Reynolds, Jim Ryerson, Howdy Sleeper, Kaja Wall, Mrs. T. P. Webster, and Tom and Marni White.

Typing of previous editions was contributed by Coral Dueber, Ginny Edwards, Mary Menzel, Joan Short, Melissa Tucker, and Diana Weddle, with the encouragement of Janet Strauss.

Printing of previous editions was accomplished by Henry Genthe, Patrick McKeon, Mary Menzel, and Diana Weddle.

We would like to thank Johnny Hart, Frank Interlandi, and Walt Kelly for allowing us to use their excellent cartoons.

G. M. C.
P. Y. S.
M. S. L.

Introduction

This is a manual for people who want to adapt their own lifestyles so as to be less a part of the environmental deterioration problem and more a part of the solution. The following suggestions are physical and psychological changes that individuals can make to ease the burden of pollution, waste, overpopulation, and resource depletion. All of these suggestions may not apply to every individual; but if the world and its populations of living creatures (including man) are to survive under habitable conditions, people, who are the greatest wasters of all, are going to have to consider lifestyles that are compatible with the earth's capabilities to sustain natural life.

The thoughts and action described herein fall into general rules of operation. THE KEY WORD IS CONSUMPTION . . . all topics discussed below are related to this activity, whether it be overconsumption, underconsumption, or nonconsumption!

The following information illustrates that consumption is the core of the immense waste problem in the United States:

⊖ More than one billion pounds of solid wastes are discarded each day in this country. This means that on the average each man, woman, and child throws away one ton yearly. Each year this waste is composed of 7 million automobiles, 100 million rubber tires, 30 million tons of paper, 4 million tons of plastics, 48 billion cans, 26 billion bottles, and hundreds of thousands of appliances such as refrigerators, washing machines, dryers, television sets, toasters, blenders, and electric toothbrushes (1, 2).*

⊖ Some of these wasted products, such as garbage, paper, and some metals, can be broken down by natural action. But many of the materials that we discard are not susceptible to such action. The amount of collected dry refuse discarded each day per person in the United States has increased from 2.75 pounds in 1920 to 5.0 pounds in 1970. It is predicted that by 1980 eight pounds per person per day of dry refuse will be collected, and by then there will be about 50 million more people discarding their wastes (2, 17). The cost of collecting this refuse (which is paid for by you!) was $3.5 billion in 1969 (2).

⊖ At present industry generally considers it less expensive to use new materials than to recycle old in making products. This is seen in the increase in use of nonreturnable glass bottles, the abandoned automobiles that scrap dealers are hesitant to salvage, the 25 million pounds of aluminum toothpaste tubes thrown away and forgotten each year . . . (1).

We have a choice of learning to dispose properly of our solid wastes or possibly of being buried by

* Numbers appearing in parentheses throughout this book refer to the numbered items under "Literature Cited," p. 115, at the end of the book.

them. It is time we brought this irrational, costly, throwaway lifestyle to a halt!

It is the responsibility of the individual to do as much as he can to ensure that his activities are ecologically efficient and result in minimum waste. The following rules describe actions that can be followed by individuals or groups of individuals in reaching this goal. We realize that one person's contribution is not going to solve the whole problem; we hope that one person's involvement will lead others to realize the importance of these actions. The personal satisfaction and enhanced quality of everyday life produced by living in closer accord with the environment are perhaps the greatest rewards one can receive. Any of these small things taken alone will *not* solve the problem, but their summation will lead to results.

General Rules to Live By

Be Constantly Aware of the Interdependence of Man and Nature.

- ⊖ Everything we do has an effect somewhere.
- ⊖ Be alert to the ultimate fate of items you use.
- ⊖ Before using, ask, "What will it do to the state of the environment?"

Use Only Those Materials Essential to Your Existence.

- ⊖ Eliminate the "I WANT" philosophy of life.
- ⊖ "Eat to live, don't live to eat."
- ⊖ Fight needless consumption; purchase only items that you really need.

Buy Durable Items, Avoiding Those Designed for Obsolescence.

- ⊖ "Make what you can, bake what you can, grow what you can."
- ⊖ Avoid "take what you can."

4

Seek to Recycle Anything You "Consume."

⊖ Reuse products rather than discard them.
⊖ Donate things that others can use.

Inform Yourself About the Activities of the Overt Despoilers of the Earth.

⊖ Question everything!

Teach Others Ecologically Sound Concepts of Living.

⊖ Begin with your own family.
⊖ Nature is the best teacher.
⊖ Learn also from books, TV specials, and conservation meetings.

Support Any Political (or Nonpolitical) Action (or Inaction) That Tends to Alleviate the Problems Facing Our Earth.

⊖ Vote, write letters, petition, boycott, testify.

Oppose the Social Myths of Growth, Progress, and Development.

⊖ There is nothing inevitable about "progress."
⊖ Natural beauty and open spaces are the common heritage of all life and should be protected from "improvements."

Fight the Social Pressures Perpetuating the Production of Large Families.

⊖ The population bomb is your baby.

Set a Good Example Yourself in Your Lifestyle, Awareness, Waste, Consumption, Reproduction, and Communication with Others.

⊖ Nothing's going to change unless we're willing to live it ourselves!

"I think she's trying to tell us, industry alone doesn't create pollution and industry alone can't clean it up!"

Resources to Be Conserved

Packaging Materials

More paper, plastics, glass, and metals are being used in packaged goods than ever before. The trend toward nondegradable, throwaway containers has already surpassed the capabilities of our solid waste disposals systems (2). Americans in 1970 will buy 60 million tons of packaging materials and will discard 90 percent of it. This figure is increasing by 6 percent a year, which is six times the rate of population increase. In 1966, an average of 575 pounds of packaging materials was used annually by each individual in the United States. By 1976 this figure will reach 661 pounds (6). The time for consumer action is now!

Aluminum and Tin Cans

Cans are made either of a tin-plated steel or of aluminum. Some "tin" cans have aluminum parts. More tin than aluminum cans are produced in the United States, but the use of aluminum for cans is increasing. Tin cans are more difficult to recycle because they are made of mixed metals and their

7

reclamation value is low; steel scrap is worth about $20 a ton whereas aluminum nets $200 a ton (3).

Although tin cans will eventually rust, they still comprise a large solid waste problem because they are not being recycled. Aluminum, on the other hand, does not break down readily and could become a significant part of the solid waste crisis if it is not recycled.

ACTION

⊖ Cut down on your use of cans, especially for beverages.

⊖ Avoid buying aerosol cans. They are dangerous and are difficult to dispose of. Sixteen percent of the cost of a product in an aerosol can goes for the container (6).

⊖ Buy bulk, dry, dog chow. Fortify the chow with unsaturated oils, bouillon, vegetables, cottage cheese, or leftovers. A single can of dogfood for each meal that Bowser eats can lead, of itself, to your own solid waste problem.

⊖ If you must buy canned goods, buy all-aluminum cans and save them to be reused. Never throw aluminum away! *Aluminum cans may be identified by the lack of side and bottom seams.*

⊖ Turn in your used aluminum items rather than disposing of them. Several aluminum and beverage manufacturers have been active in and responsive to the movement to recycle aluminum and are buying it from individuals and groups for 10¢ a pound. This comes to approximately ½¢ per can. These centers will also take other items such as TV trays, pie pans, lawn furniture, aluminum foil, or anything else that is all aluminum.

⊖ Aluminum foil should be used, reused, reused again, and then recycled.

⊖ Put your pop-top inside the can as soon as you have pulled the tab. Pop-tops not only create litter, but are a danger to unwary fish and diving birds, which mistake them for fish and eat them.

⊖ Call local scrap metal and salvage companies to find out whether they will purchase aluminum (or tin cans if enough are collected).
SCRAP METAL DEALER:_____

⊖ If you know of no dealer in your area that is buying used aluminum, contact one of the following companies that have been cooperating in this venture:

Reynolds Aluminum
Company
P.O. Box 2346 LI
Richmond, Va. 23218

Adolph Coors Company
pany
Golden, Colo. 80401

⊖ Make profits for your community group by picking up and selling aluminum. One YMCA group in Manhattan, Kans., earned $1522 for collecting 350,000 aluminum cans (4). Ideal places for pick-up sites are grocery stores, shopping centers, gas stations, schools, and churches.

⊖ Check to see if there is an ecology-minded group in your area that is already collecting and recycling aluminum (and maybe tin). Try the local newspaper, Junior Chamber of Com-

merce, university or college, the Scouts, and the YMCA.
ALUMINUM RECYCLING CENTER:____

Glass Bottles and Jars

The contribution of glass to the solid waste mess is immense. Approximately 28 billion bottles are *thrown away* each year in the United States. Glass makes up 6 percent of municipal waste (5). The need for returning to the returnables is immediate! The public's belief that used containers will simply disappear is escapism of the worst sort!

In 1950, the average returnable bottle made 31 trips between the user and the manufacturer. Today, each bottle, on the average, makes only 19 round trips (5). In New York two years ago, Pepsi distributed 14.4 million new returnable bottles and raised the deposit to 5¢. Within six months they had all been disposed of by the public! What kind of common sense is being exhibited here? We all need to reuse, not waste, our precious resources.

A trend back to returnable bottles might lead to the standardization of the many sizes and shapes of bottles, which would greatly enhance the feasibility of the reuse of these containers by all companies.

Meanwhile, used glass is being incorporated into "glasphalt" surfacing for roadways, runways, and walkways. Glass is substituted for the sand in asphalt, making it more durable. We do not favor the construction of any new concrete jungles, but possibly this project will aid in repairing already existing roads.

ACTION

⊖ Buy only returnable bottles!

⊖ Return them!

⊖ Support manufacturers that sell deposit bottles. Write them and express your satisfaction with this policy. Some products that come in deposit bottles:

All returnable	*Some returnable*
Par-T-Pak	Seven-Up
Cragmont	Coca Cola
Dr. Pepper	Canada Dry
RC Cola	Pepsi Cola
Nehi	
Diet-Rite	
Yukon Club	

⊖ Write those companies that DO NOT make returnable bottles, expressing your displeasure and your boycott of their products. There has been a general trend to avoid selling beer in deposit bottles. Write letters to these bottlers relating your concern.

⊖ Buy beer in tappers or kegs. Approach your local winery or wine dealer with the idea of selling bulk wine from a keg. Fill your own reusable bottles from it. In some areas there are legal barriers to this procedure. Attempt to change these laws.

⊖ Reuse jars for other purposes, such as storing nuts and bolts, leftovers, canning or freezing fruits and vegetables. Also, good jars with sealable lids may be helpful to museums or biological research institutes for storing preserved specimens.

⊖ Baby food jars are uniform in size and shape and have resealable lids, and therefore are ideal for holding other homemade products. Thirty-six percent of the cost of each jar of baby food pays for the container alone (6).

⊖ To avoid baby food jars, make your own baby food. Write the John Oster Manufacturing Company in Milwaukee, Wis. 53217, for a booklet on home preparation of baby food.

⊖ Contact the Glass Container Manufacturers Institute, 330 Madison Avenue, New York, N.Y. 10017, about their glass reclamation program, which pays ½¢ for each bottle or jar returned. They melt these down and make new containers out of them. There are an increasing number of reclamation centers in urban areas, so ask GCMI for the address of the center nearest you.

⊖ Call the bottling companies listed in the yellow pages of your telephone book to obtain information about local glass recycling programs. If these companies are not engaged in bottle reclamation, write to their national offices and express your concern and your interest in channels for bottle reuse.

⊖ Ban disposable bottles at all governmental levels. Finland, British Columbia (5), and Bowie, Md., have all passed laws against throwaway bottles. For copies of the Bowie ordinance, contact Mayor Leo E. Green, Bowie City Hall, Bowie, Md. 20715.

⊖ Inform your legislators of your support for programs designed to alleviate these problems! The need for constructive legislation in this area is evident

By permission of John Hart and Field Enterprises, Inc.

Plastics

The ever-increasing use of plastics as containers poses the dual problems of overconsumption of a nonrenewable resource and production of nondegradable waste. Right now 3 percent by weight of our packaging material is plastic, and the percentage is growing (1).

Plastics are made from petroleum products, a limited resource optimistically estimated to last only 70 to 80 more years (8).

Upon being incinerated, plastics tend to melt rather than burn and can foul incinerator grates. Polyvinyl chloride (PVC plastic), which is being increasingly incorporated into packaging, produces hydrochloric acid when burned. This is a threat to plant life as well as incerator stacks (7).

There is recent evidence that protein substances, such as blood in blood banks, absorb the plasticizer from plastic (PVC) storage bags. The plasticizers then accumulate in "significant quantities" in the spleen, liver, lung, and abdominal fat in transfused patients. Such plasticizers have been found to have subtle toxic effects on cells in culture (18). Much more research needs to be done in this area, but it appears that it may be advantageous to health to use as few plastic bags and containers and as little plastic wrap as possible when storing meat, milk, cheese, and other protein foods.

Plastic is now flooding the market in the form of containers for liquid bleach, liquid detergents, juices, and milk. The chemical compositions of these varied plastics are so diverse that melting and reusing them would be technically too complex to be practical. However, Dow Chemical Corporation in San Diego has developed a technique for reusing *similar* kinds of milk containers for making agricultural rain gutters. This kind of recycling can be accomplished only by using uniform types of containers that can be readily collected in large enough quantities to make reprocessing economically feasible. They must also be easily transported to the site of reprocessing. The plastic bottles being recycled by Dow are made of ADPE, which is worth about $120 to $160 per ton (9).

The beverage industry keeps threatening to produce soda pop in plastic bottles. This kind of negligent packaging can be accepted only if there is a strong guarantee that these containers will be recycled. Some innovations are being studied whereby a "self-destructing" plastic bottle will be produced. This would have drawbacks in that it is one-way use of a resource and may not break down under all conditions.

ACTION

⊖ Avoid buying plastics in any form.
⊖ If you must buy plastics, purchase only those products that are intended to last. Keep reusing them!
⊖ Do not accept plastic bags at the grocery store or dry cleaners.
⊖ Obtain as few plastic bags as possible; wash, dry and reuse them several times. When your newspaper is delivered in a waterproof bag, use it; don't just throw it away. Plastic bags

can be used as galoshes or instant briefcases in rainy weather.

⊖ Use a durable metal tape dispenser rather than disposable plastic ones.

⊖ Ball-point and felt-tip pens are wasteful. Fountain pens last forever and can be economically refilled.

⊖ When purchasing a typewriter, be sure to choose one that automatically rewinds and re-uses ribbon. Those that discard ribbons after one use are wasteful.

⊖ Buy only those plastic toys that are built to last. Pass them on!

⊖ Do not allow such items as combs, toothbrushes, hair brushes, or plastic tampon cylinders to enter your toilet, as they can cause clogging and damage both in your plumbing and at the sewage treatment facility.

⊖ Collect Styrofoam egg and meat containers. Return them to the dairy or meat market responsible. Specifically ask for fresh meat wrapped in paper rather than in plastic.

⊖ Complain to and, if necessary, boycott eating establishments (especially the take-out variety) that waste such items as plastic forks and spoons, condiment and relish containers (for catsup, mayonnaise, mustard, and so on), straws, and Styrofoam cups.

⊖ Avoid using disposable plastic forks and spoons, cups, and so on, at home and on picnics.

⊖ Do not purchase frozen foods packaged in plastic cooking pouches.

⊖ Address your complaints and inquiries about plastics to the Society of the Plastics Industry, 250 Park Avenue, New York, N.Y. 10017.

Wax-Cardboard Containers

The wax-cardboard type of container, including milk cartons, cottage cheese, yogurt, or sour cream containers, and some meat and delicatessen packages, presents much the same wastage problem as paper, but the same channels for recycling do not exist.

ACTION

- Buy products in as large a container as possible without letting its contents spoil.
- Reuse these containers for storage of leftovers, freezing of home-grown vegetables or other food materials, or for lunch pail food containers.
- Milk cartons and cardboard cans from frozen juice concentrate are especially good candle molds.
- Grow cuttings and seedlings in cartons that have been cut either vertically or horizontally to form small flats or pots for individual plants.
- Store kitchen drippings in these cartons and take them to stores that will buy them for lard. These drippings include kitchen grease, bacon fat, cooking oils. Better yet, save these and use them in making your own soap (see page 58, under FOOD SCRAPS).
- Call your local dairies and inquire about the availability of returnable glass bottles. ADDRESS OF LOCAL DAIRY SELLING PRODUCTS IN REUSABLE (GLASS OR PLASTIC) CONTAINERS:_____

Shopping Bags

Shopping bags represent one of the most obvious wastes of a resource (trees) going. Any store that doesn't offer free bags, and double ones or individual ones for each vegetable at that, is considered not to be serving the customer. We believe that customers would be better served if they brought their own reusable shopping bags.

ACTION

⊖ Support stores, if you find any, that do not give away paper bags. Perhaps if customers were charged 5¢ a bag, more would be encouraged to bring their own shopping bags or at least to reuse the paper ones.

⊖ Refuse bags at the grocery store and tell them why. This eventually may lead to an increase in ecological awareness among those who observe your actions.

⊖ Take your own shopping bags with you. These can be the stretchable net type, used for many years by European shoppers, or canvas bags. You can make your own canvas bag or check with your local ecology center (if there is one in your locale). If you don't have an ecology center, start one. If they don't offer canvas shopping bags, go into the business and make them yourself. The ecology symbol emblazoned on the side of the bag would serve as an additional indication of your awareness of our waste problem.

⊖ If you accept some paper bags, use them to the utmost—for lunches, lining garbage pails, and so on, and use them several times where possible. They also make good wrapping paper for postal packages.

⊖ Give your used paper bags (those that you took before you became ecologically aware) to stores that reuse them. In many communities there are bread outlets that sell bakery products that are seconds or are day-old. These places often run on a tight budget and cannot afford to give paper bags away. Ask your Salvation Army Store and similar secondhand stores if they need bags.

⊖ Use a lunch box instead of a paper bag.

Wood and Paper Products

Wood

Our supply of timber is becoming rapidly depleted, especially because of the increasing demand for building materials and paper products. The scarcity of wood is so great that the lumber industry proposed a National Timber Supply Act that would have allowed additional cutting of timber in certain of our National Forest areas. This legislation was fortunately defeated, but it clearly indicates that wood is a very limited resource that takes many years to regenerate.

ACTION

⊖ If you are planning to build a new home, think about building one of nonwood materials such as cinder block, brick, stone, or adobe.

⊖ How about buying and fixing up an old or even

© Field Enterprises, Inc., 1970

2-18

By permission of John Hart and Field Enterprises, Inc.

abandoned house instead of building a new one?

⊖ Consider the possibility of using wood (and other materials) from abandoned and disintegrating dwellings for your home improvements. Be sure to get the owner's approval before undertaking such an endeavor, and offer to pay for the wood. Driftwood can also be a useful source of building material.

⊖ Build a dome, build with foam, or even carve a house in the side of a hill. The *Whole Earth Catalog* (*see* PERIODICALS, page 110) has much useful information on these techniques.

⊖ Avoid purchasing firewood. Paying people to go out and cut down trees (or cutting them yourself) for use in fireplaces is a luxury our forests can ill afford. Many lumber yards give away lumber scraps that make fine firewood. Construction sites are another good source, and many foremen will give you permission to pick up their lumber leftovers. In many areas, driftwood on beaches or fallen wood in forests are in plentiful supply.

⊖ Invite a live Christmas tree into your home this year. Forty to sixty million Christmas trees were butchered and discarded last year (42). You can keep a small tree in a pot for several years, or replant it after the holiday. Have the city plant it in a park if a yard is not available. In some cities, living Christmas trees can be rented.

Newspapers

Most paper is derived from wood, and much timber is wasted in the form of paper products. Each person in the United States discards 540 pounds of paper each year (12). Many paper products can be easily recycled by the consumer and therefore present an area in which individual effort can have a marked effect.

Newspapers are both a source of much wasted paper and a material that can easily lend itself to recycling. In Los Angeles County, 10 million pounds of paper are thrown away each day. The major portion of this wastage is newspapers and magazines (11). Furthermore, at least one third to one half of every daily newspaper is not read by the subscriber, and journalists even use "filler" items rather than trying to conserve space, the reader's time, and paper.

In West Germany 33 percent of the waste paper is recycled; in Japan 46 percent! In 1966, in the United States, 10 million tons of waste paper were recycled, resulting in 10,000 jobs worth $45 million in salaries and a saving of 12,800,000 cords (13 million acres of trees) that did not have to be cut (13). *However*, this amount of recycled paper amounts to only 10 or 20 percent of the total paper production in this country. The need is evident for an efficient, widely based system of reusing waste paper.

ACTION

⊖ Support advertisers that use small, concise ads, and especially support nonadvertisers, those who don't advertise at all.

⊖ Inform stores that use frequent, large, space- and paper-wasting ads that they do not deserve your patronage, and explain that they are wasting a valuable resource (paper = trees). It is estimated that one ton of newspapers is the equivalent of 17 trees (12).

⊖ Save and bundle your newspapers. Newspapers come in a form that is easily stockpiled and returned directly to the original source. It is plentiful, makes a compact bundle, and weighs enough to make its transportation to even a relatively distant reclamation site economically rewarding.

⊖ Contact your local paper reclamation center. Local recycling programs for waste paper have been spreading over the entire country in the last few years. Service groups made some $9 million from selling used papers to the plant in Alsip, Ill. (12). Your community possibly has groups that are already collecting and selling paper to processing plants. Likely groups such as the Scouts and "Y" clubs can usually be found in the yellow pages under "clubs," "service clubs," or "organizations."
PAPER RECLAMATION CENTER: _____

_____

⊖ Start a recycling program. Successful recycling programs take a lot of work but can be very satisfying. They require organization, faithful volunteers, available heavy-duty transportation, and a good information program to inform the public so that support is guaranteed. It has been our experience in southern California that public support can be overwhelming, even to the extent that volunteer operations cannot handle the load!

⊖ Work toward municipal handling of paper reclamation. Ultimately, solid waste recycling will have to be handled by municipal operations with the support of all citizens. In the long run, this kind of operation will pay off because the present policy of filling empty canyons with wastes will cost more, in both financial and environmental ways, than recycling operations that defray some of their cost by selling the reusable materials.

⊖ Work toward enacting legislation that will eliminate waste of our resources and facilitate their reuse. Adequate sorting and processing facilities must be provided by local governmental bodies. The technology is available (see pages 30–36) for solid waste reuse techniques.

⊖ Use recycled paper for your communications. Recycling of paper won't work unless there is a market. Ask your paper dealer for Allied and Bergstrom recycled paper.

Magazines and Telephone Books

Magazines and telephone books are not acceptable to the groups that recycle newspapers, primarily because of their composition and the amount of clay used to make the pages shiny. There are several things that WE CAN DO about them.

ACTION

⊖ Share magazines. Why should every person in a neighborhood (or in the same office) buy the same magazine? Set up a system whereby each neighbor buys one magazine subscription and then circulates the magazines among the group.

⊖ Pass magazines on to libraries, service organizations, youth groups, and laundromats. Barbershops and the waiting rooms of doctors' offices and hospitals would be eager to accept donations of magazines. Check with the schools in your area to see if teachers can use them as reading material or to make displays and collages.

⊖ Approach the various paper companies or the distributors to convince them to devise and implement means of reusing magazines.

⊖ Interest the telephone company in picking up the old books when the new ones are issued and in making arrangements with their paper supplier to reuse the paper from the old books. (This is presently done in some parts of the country.)

⊖ Reuse telephone books as coloring books for children or as material for making useful papier-mâché objects.

Books

Much useful information is contained in books, even older ones. Books, however, are intended for use, whether as a reference source or as an entertaining way to spend some time.

ACTION

⊖ Buy only those books that you intend to read.

⊖ Instead of stockpiling unused books, lend them to friends and keep them circulating. You can always borrow them back, and it is a terrible waste for each of us to have a copy that sits on the shelf and gathers dust.

⊖ Cut down on your book consumption by using the local libraries. They buy books for you to read and you are paying the bill for these public services.

⊖ Donate used books to libraries. If a book is a worthy addition, they will possibly rebind it, if necessary, and put it on the shelves. If they cannot use it, they will either sell it, burn it, or store it in some unused room. Before donating such books, be sure you know the ultimate destination of your donation. School libraries and youth organizations also appreciate book donations, especially those that pertain to subjects relating to the membership.

⊖ Resell books to campus bookstores. They will generally return 50 percent of the value of a book that is still being used as a text for a class. They will pay between 20¢ and $1.00 for paperbacks originally costing less than $2.50. Hardbacks will bring 15 to 20 percent of the original value.

⊖ Support dealers of used books. Sell them your unneeded books and buy used books that strike your interest. Also, many fine books can be obtained at garage sales, rummage sales, and estate sales.

Stationery, Cards, and Wrapping

Much wastage occurs in the overuse of paper in the form of envelopes, letterheads, and notepads. Curtailing the wasteful use of these materials could be helpful.

ACTION

- ⊖ Write on both sides of the page. If your paper is too thin, buy paper that is a bit thicker next time.
- ⊖ Use French Notes (the foldable stationery that makes into its own envelope) such as those sold by the Post Office for overseas airmail letters.
- ⊖ Christmas cards are large offenders. Try to avoid sending them, or at least send only those that will be appreciated. For friends or family who are far away and to whom a card might mean a lot, send one with little paper (a fold-over or postcard) that conveys thought and goodwill.
- ⊖ Use the backs of used sheets of paper for note-pads. If you like to take notes while talking on the phone, have a blackboard handy. It can be used and erased MANY times.
- ⊖ Use as little gift wrapping as possible. Wrap presents in newspapers, the Sunday comics, or old, recovered wrappings from previous gifts. This will not only save you money but will soothe your pollution-conscious mind. Gifts can also be wrapped in towels or fabric, which can then be used by the recipient. Children delight in using their paintings as gift wrap. The same philosophy should be followed when using ribbon and bows for gift wrappings. Use them over and over again. Yarn ties have lots of uses. Store packages that gifts come in, one inside another, in a dry place for future use.
- ⊖ Save old note paper, greeting cards, bits of ribbon and yarn, and so on, to use in making

your own gift cards or for children to make cutouts and collages. Nursery schools and kindergartens often need egg cartons, cardboard rollers from toilet paper and paper towels, buttons, small plastic and paper containers, baby food jars, and all sorts of things.

Advertising

Each of us is besieged by a daily onslaught of advertising in the mail that is as irritating as it is wasteful. There are two forms of third-class advertising involved: unsolicited ads, which are addressed to "occupant" or a similar loose designation, and mailing-list ads, which are addressed to you by name.

ACTION

- ⊖ Return unsolicited ads to the sender. The Post Office can stop placing them in your mail upon request, but they will merely be thrown away at the Post Office. Explain to the sender why you do not wish to receive them. Inform him that continued receipt of his ads will force you to deny him your business.
- ⊖ The Post Office *can* help with mailing list advertisements. Inform the Post Office that you want to be taken off any specific mailing list that has offended you. Obtain Form 2150. Explain, in filling out this form, why you feel it to be a pandering advertisement. Tell them why you will refuse any further mail.

- ⊖ If the ad is marked "return postage guaranteed," or something similar, you can mark it "refused" and it will be returned at the advertiser's expense.
- ⊖ Fill return postpaid envelopes with the offending ad and a letter stating your objections and mail back to the advertiser.
- ⊖ Support legislation that will prevent the Department of Motor Vehicles (and other governmental agencies) from selling your name and address to potential advertisers.
- ⊖ Make your legislators aware of the magnitude of this problem by saving your "junk mail" and sending the accumulation to your congressman, explaining your dismay.

Miscellaneous Paper Products

Products such as toilet paper, paper towels, and paper napkins are being used in greater quantities than ever because of "convenience." However, this may ultimately lead to disastrous proportions of paper residues over much of the earth. It has been reported that a "gray band" covering the surface of the Atlantic Ocean as far as 20 miles out from the coast has been partly attributed to a high concentration of cellulose fibers from toilet paper remaining in the water after discharge from sewage outfalls (14). This cover can prevent some penetration of sunlight through the surface waters, thus depriving the phytoplankton of their energy source. The result may be a serious problem for food chains in the affected areas. A further complication is that few marine animals have the cellulose-breaking enzyme cellulase in their digestive systems.

ACTION

⊖ Use as few paper products as possible. Reuse what you can—a paper towel that is used to soak up water can be dried and reused.

⊖ Use cloth napkins and towels. They can be added to other washing with a negligible additional use of water and cleanser.

⊖ Reuse the wax paper liners of cereal boxes as wrapping material for foods.

⊖ Use cloth or durable plastic placemats instead of paper ones.

⊖ Take tin or ceramic place settings to picnics and parties instead of using disposable paper plates, cups, and other containers.

⊖ Avoid disposable diapers and diaper liners. They represent one of the best examples of the unnecessary waste in our society.

⊖ Reuse cardboard boxes. Large department and grocery stores sometimes bale the cardboard and sell it to paper processing companies. Boxes can be used over and over again as containers. Don't throw them away; they are useful.

⊖ Do not flush paper products down toilets. They can cause dreadful results in plumbing as well as in sewage treatment plants. Offending items include rags, large paper towels, cardboard cylinders of tampons, and disposable diapers and diaper liners. Avoid using these, but by all means DO NOT FLUSH them!

Solid Waste Disposal

It has become abundantly clear in the preceding sections that we have a tremendous solid waste problem in the United States. Trash could be a big business. However, it is presently not regarded as a resource, but as an expensive, land-gobbling, polluting, disposal problem. The general solution is to haul trash to sanitary landfills, compact it, and bury it. The landfill thus created will one day be the base for a housing development or possibly a golf course. In the meantime, a beautiful NATURAL canyon or field has been filled up with our waste materials. Another solution, often used in conjunction with a landfill, is incineration. This has been a limited solution owing to the air pollution created. However, new incineration techniques involving high temperatures may help solve this problem. Incineration will always be wasteful, though, because the combusted materials cannot be recycled.

Far more practical are the recently developed recycling operations for materials that are sufficiently valuable to bring some profit, including paper, cardboard, tin and aluminum cans, bottles, and various scrap metals such as copper and brass (49). In World War II, paper, aluminum, rubber, animal fat, and other resources were recycled voluntarily by each citizen. When the war ended, the need for this type of conservation seemed less pressing, and the practice was eliminated. Many informed people have been attempting to reactivate this solution to our ever-increasing solid waste crisis. Service groups are now sponsoring the recycling of many of these materials, and some municipalities operate their own programs.

Recycling Centers

If there is no recycling center in your community, band together some interested groups and start one! There are several basic steps to establishing an effective center.

Ascertain the quantity of material available in your area for recycling, i.e., how much newspaper is produced locally? Is the source sufficient to warrant your involvement?

Determine how much of the available material can actually be collected. There are several methods to contemplate: house-to-house collecting, central retrieval sites, such as supermarkets, or periodic stations, such as church meetings or conservation club meetings.

Arrange for a work force large enough to handle the material. These people must be interested and enthusiastic enough to sustain the program over a long time span. Too often initial interest quickly wanes, leaving the program undermanned.

Make sure that there is a market within a reasonable distance for the materials you are collecting. For aluminum, check with local beer companies or the companies and associations listed under aluminum and tin cans in this book. Try the same approach for bottles, papers, and so on.

Transportation is essential to the operation. Be sure that you have large enough vehicles to haul materials in quantities large enough to be economically rewarding, and that the vehicles will be available whenever needed. People will become discouraged if they see that items they have brought in for recycling just sit in the bin at the recycling center week after week.

Publicity is also desirable. Let people in the area know the reasons for recycling efforts and locations where items are collected. Emphasize the need for volunteers, but keep in mind that the operation is usually smoother and more reliable if at least some workers are on payroll.

Use a recycling symbol to publicize your group's activities. Two such symbols are pictured below. Place these symbols on collection bins, and urge manufacturers to mark them on products that should be recycled.

Recycling symbol designed by Gary Anderson for a contest sponsored by The Container Corporation of America.

Recycling symbol used by Get Oil Out (G.O.O.) in their community recycling program in Santa Barbara, California.

Municipal Operations

At this writing, there are few efficiently operating recycling centers in the United States. In Europe, however, there are many (49). The technology is available, but it remains for public interest to encourage officials to demand this rational approach to waste disposal. The Federal government spends about $15.9 million per year (8¢ per person) on solid waste management while $3.1 *billion* ($14.76 per person per year) goes for space travel (42). We need to reorder our priorities. Ecology, like charity, must begin at home.

Recycling materials from municipal trash will serve to allay some of the cost of disposing of our solid wastes. In France it is estimated that 50 tons of trash per eight-hour day can be turned into compost, with the gas given off used to run turbines for power generation. This operation costs $120,000 per year and employs two men. The resulting net loss is only about 10¢ a ton, compared with $2.50 a ton for an average sanitary landfill (49). Therefore, municipal recycling is economically feasible as well as environmentally sound.

Plastic garbage bags are handy in that they make less noise and are easier for the sanitary engineers to handle, but they are a pollution and disposal problem in themselves. New devices designed to crush your trash into small squares do aid somewhat in the pick-up and transportation process, but they use an excessive amount of electric power and make it virtually impossible to separate valuable materials.

ACTION

⊖ Encourage trash separation programs (as during wartime) in which families separate their own trash into paper, cans, and wet garbage. Trash can then be dealt with more efficiently, and much of it can be recycled.

⊖ Urge that some of the engineering talent formerly employed in aerospace be utilized to develop more efficient methods of trash pick-up, transport, and recycling.

⊖ Meanwhile, recycle your own trash: organic stuff to the compost pile, newspapers to the pulp mill, cans to aluminum companies or scrap dealers, and bottles to the Glass Containers Manufacturers center near you. If these are not available, start writing letters.

⊖ Support private enterprise that attempts to get into the business of reusing materials obtainable from trash.

⊖ Encourage stores and businesses to obtain a shredder that will chop up used paper goods into a form saleable to pulp mills. Support stores that are already using this technique on their cardboard boxes.

⊖ Ideas regarding disposability of products such as autos and appliances were offered in bill HR 17132. They include—

A disposal tax to be placed on nonconsumable products that will reflect the actual cost of disposing or recycling the materials (e.g., about $100 per auto).

Encouragement of industry to develop ways to refine and use recycled matter. Most of the techniques are available and merely need to be made operable.

The posting of a $100 bond by a person buying a car or appliance, which will be passed on to each successive owner at full face value. The money would be refunded when the item was turned over to the proper center, where much of it would be recycled.

Petroleum Products

Petroleum is one of our fastest-disappearing resources, and we must make every effort to cut our high rate of consumption. With 90 million cars in the United States (nearly one for every two citizens!), we are presently going through oil and gasoline at an exorbitant rate. This, too, is an area in which individual action can be very effective in minimizing the problem.

Transportation

We look forward to the advent of the noninternal combustion engine and are cheered by indications that help is on the way. But meanwhile there is much that we can do to lessen gasoline consumption with cars that are currently available.

ACTION

⊖ Drive less! Walk, ride a bike, jog, or "get a horse." This will not only conserve resources but will improve health and spirits. Bike riders can point to the conservational aspects of this activity by obtaining (from your local ecology center) or making a knapsack marked with the ⊖symbol of ecology and the legend POLLU-TION SOLUTION.

⊖ Urge establishment of bike trails and lanes. Have bike racks placed in shopping and business centers.

⊖ Check among your neighbors and coworkers to find people who can readily share rides. It is much more efficient to have many bodies transported in one car than many cars with only one body each. But take a look around you at all the lonely drivers! If you work at a large enough place, establish an information center where people who wish to share rides can get together (a computer makes this ridiculously easy).

⊖ Use mass transit systems whenever possible. If there is a sufficient demand for this kind of service, new routes will be established to meet people's needs. Any form of rapid transit will more efficiently use our natural resources and therefore should be planned, supported, and utilized.

⊖ Buy a car only if you need it. One of the present bases of the petroleum consumption problem is the social pressure to gain status by acquiring more, bigger, and newer cars. The social myth of "a car in every garage" has been updated to "two cars (at least) in every garage," and it's long past time to end this trend.

⊖ Buy only as much car as you need. Most of us need neither the high speed nor the colossal power which are regarded as selling points

By permission of John Hart and Field Enterprises, Inc.

for the majority of our cars. When buying a car, seek one that is powered by a small, high-efficiency engine that burns less gas per mile. Also be sure that the car you purchase has effective smog-control features.

⊖ Support legislation that will set a maximum limit on the size (displacement) of car engines, put a tax penalty on larger cars, or even increase the price of gasoline.

Power Generation and Use

Ninety-eight percent of the electrical power generated in the United States comes from the burning of fossil fuels (60 percent from oil and gas, 38 percent from coal). Therefore, our use of electricity directly relates to the consumption of our limited petroleum resources, and our national demand for electricity has been doubling every six to ten years, far outstripping the population growth (15)! The magnitude of the problem was starkly demonstrated by the "brownout" in New York during the summer of 1970.

Atomic power, often touted as an alternative to fossil fuel use, may create more problems than it solves. These problems include thermal pollution, radioactive contamination, and ultimate dumping of radioactive waste.

ACTION

⊖ Before buying any sort of electrical appliance, do some soul searching. Remember General Rule Number 2: "Use only those materials essential to your existence." Much of the increase in power consumption comes from advertising's creation of a "need" for hordes of "convenience" appliances. Most of us would have trouble justifying the purchase and use of appliances to perform simple chores like opening cans, brushing teeth, manicuring nails, and so on.

⊖ Avoid the appliances most advertised by electrical companies and manufacturers. They are, in fact, among the worst offenders in terms of power consumption and expense to the user. These appliances include electric water heaters, electric heaters, electric ranges, electric dryers, air conditioners, and electric frost-free refrigerators and freezers (16).

⊖ Shop wisely. If you decide that an appliance is truly necessary for you, select the one that will use the least power to do the job. Different brands and models of similar appliances have different wattage ratings that indicate the amount of power required to run them. The wattage rating is marked on a small metal plate on each heavy appliance. Multiply the wattage rating by the amount of time the power must be on to do the job. The lower the product of this multiplication (kilowatt-hours), the more efficient the machine.

⊖ If you use a dish- or clothes-washer, always wash full loads (this also saves water and cleanser). Whenever possible, dry clothes outside, rather than in a dryer. The clothes come out brighter, and you use less electricity.

⊖ It does *not* take extra power to turn on a light bulb. When it's on, it is using electricity; when it's off, it is not. So turn out the lights when you leave a room or quit reading. Besides, candles are nice, and you can make them yourself.

⊖ Turning a light off and on often does tend to shorten the life of the bulb. Avoid this other waste of resources and fight planned obsolescence at the same time by buying "lifetime" or at least "5-year" bulbs. These are available at some local hardware and builder's supply stores. Get your store managers to stock bulbs with a 130-volt rating, which are much longer lasting than the 120-volt ones commonly sold, and do not use appreciably more electricity.

⊖ Don't leave TV's, stereos, radios, and other appliances running when you are not actually using them, and avoid using them merely to provide background noise on which your attention isn't really focused. Use heaters only when necessary. It's easier on the environment to put on a sweater or some slippers than to turn the thermostat up another notch. Keep your fireplace damper closed to prevent heat loss.

Air

Clean air is one of the most important resources in our daily lives, but it is one that is becoming exceedingly scarce, particularly in urban areas. Air pollution is such an important national problem that it was extensively dealt with by the President's Council on Environmental Quality, which opens its discussion thus:

Air pollution adversely affects man and his environment in many ways. It soils his home and interferes with the growth of plants and shrubs. It diminishes the value of his agricultural products. It obscures his view, and adds unpleasant smells to his environment. Most important, it endangers his health (2).

In order to realistically attack this problem, we need to know the basic kinds and causes of air pollution.

Particulate pollutants include such things as dust, ash, soot, and smoke. They can be produced by everything from burning leaves in your backyard to the smokestacks of a local factory. In the whole United States, industrial processes account for the production of 27 percent of particulate pollutants, while stationary fuel combustion (power generation, burning fossil fuels for heating of homes and businesses, and so on) accounts for 31 percent. Forest fires account for 8 percent. This is the very visible aspect of air pollution. It is ugly, gets things and people dirty, absorbs and scatters sunlight, cuts down visibility, and irritates and annoys people.

Other air pollutants are primarily present in the form of gases and aerosols. Aerosols are the product of reactions involving hydrocarbons and other gases in the presence of sunlight. They exist as small droplets of liquid that may remain in the atmosphere for some time. The three main sources of these pollutants are transportation, power generation, and industry. Transportation contributes large portions of carbon monoxide, hydrocarbons, and nitrogen oxide emissions. Power generation is responsible for large quantities of sulfur oxides and nitrogen oxides. Industrial processes add further amounts of carbon monoxide and sulfur oxides (2).

Whereas particulate air pollution is ugly, many of the aerosols and gases are invisible, but they can be highly toxic. Carbon monoxide may cause drowsiness in conentrations commonly found in city air, thus increasing accidents. It can also aggravate blood and circulatory disorders, not to mention its

BELOW OLYMPUS   By Interlandi

"Remember when smokestacks were a sign of prosperity?"

potential for being fatal in itself. Sulfur oxides can cause temporary and permanent injury to human respiratory systems. Hydrocarbons and nitrogen oxides play a major role in forming photochemical smog, which causes eye and lung irritation. These chemicals also have harmful effects on vegetation (2).

The main sources of air pollutants of all kinds are industry, power generation, and vehicles, and action must be directed at all sources simultaneously. Most of us are drivers, so keep in mind that 42 percent of all air pollutants, by weight, come from motor vehicles.

ACTION

⊖ Work for legislation that will limit the maximum allowable level of air pollutants of all types leaving any industrial or power plant, with effective enforcement procedures and stiff penalties. Such legislation is apparently the most effective way to curb these polluters. For example, a new power plant in the California desert is expected to produce 13,000 pounds of sulfur dioxide per *hour* and 12,000 pounds per hour of nitrogen dioxide. If the same plant were located in Los Angeles County, it would be allowed to emit only 200 pounds per hour of sulfur dioxide and 140 pounds per hour of nitrogen dioxide. Legislation is an obvious and necessary first step at local, state, and national levels. So write and fight for cleaner air!

⊖ Keep your car in tune. If it is running properly, it will more efficiently burn the fuel, allowing fewer by-products to reach the atmosphere.

⊖ Be open-minded toward alternatives to petroleum-using engines. Our present automobiles can be converted to use propane or butane fuel. These fuels burn much more cleanly than gasoline, cause less engine wear, and are much more economical. Look in your yellow pages under "Gas—Liquefied Petroleum, Bottled and

Bulk" to find local companies doing this type of conversion.

⊖ Cars with noninternal combustion engines will be in production in the next few years; greet them enthusiastically!

⊖ Use a hand- or battery-powered lawnmower.

⊖ Don't smoke; it pollutes you as well as the air.

⊖ When in the woods, obey Smokey the Bear. Forest fires are a significant source of smoke pollution, as well as a loss of needed forest.

⊖ Compost leaves rather than burn them (see COMPOSTING, pp. 59–60). Scarsdale, N.Y., has a public lot where everyone may bring leaves to be composted (42).

⊖ Beware of ads from industries, power companies, and petroleum manufacturers that claim to be doing great things toward combating air pollution. Get the hard, cold facts first and then decide for yourself whether they are doing a good job. If not, don't buy their products, and let them know how shallow you have found their claims to be.

Water

Conservation of Water

In many localities, water is becoming a limiting resource. This problem results from an increased number of users and from rising requirements for water by each individual user. In 1900, 525 gallons of water per day were used for each individual. This figure is expected to reach 2,000 gallons per day per person by 1980! (20). The gravity of this problem is aggravated by the fact that local water supplies are often unpotable owing to industrial and municipal pollution.

When cities develop in the warm, dry climates considered most ideal for human habitation, the water supply often becomes insufficient to satisfy the increasing demands of the burgeoning populace. An excellent example of this situation is in California, where aqueducts are being constructed to carry large amounts of water from the wet, sparsely populated north to the dry, overpopulated south. Potential damage to aquatic systems in the north and unchecked, unplanned further growth in the south were not taken into account; this will plague future generations. Conserve water at home. Household water-use habits and small leaks can cause large amounts of water to be wasted.

ACTION

- ⊖ Don't wash dishes in running water. You can waste as much as 30 gallons of water each meal. (If you have an automatic dishwasher, wash only full loads to save water).

- ⊖ Take brief showers instead of filling the tub; you can save as much as 20 gallons of water. Take 3-minute showers or 2-inch-deep baths. Shower with a friend (or a relative)!

- ⊖ Running water to make it hot or cold can waste a gallon or more. Keep a bottle of water in the refrigerator for drinking purposes. While waiting for running water to get hot, use it for other functions such as brushing teeth, combing hair, or washing hands.

- ⊖ Be sure that your faucets don't leak. A dripping faucet can mean that as much as 25 gallons of water are wasted each day. Generally such leaks can be repaired simply by replacing the plastic or rubber washers without calling a costly plumber.

⊖ Avoid unnecessary washing with large amounts of running water. When washing your car, use a bucket and sponge, thus allowing less water to run down the street. Use a broom to clean the sidewalk and driveway; hose them only when absolutely necessary.

⊖ Flushing your toilet requires as much as 6 gallons per flush (55). Flush your toilet less often; you need not flush, for instance, every time you dispose of a cleansing tissue by dropping it into the toilet. You can also put a brick into the tank to decrease the amount of water wasted per flush without decreasing flushing efficiency. If you have even a minimal amount of mechanical ability, you can bend the arm on the float in the tank, thus letting less water in to fill the tank after each flush.

⊖ Plan your garden around native plants and varieties that are well adapted to live with only the natural rainfall of your area.

⊖ Water lawns and plants in the early evening to cut down on the amount of water lost by evaporation. Do not overwater.

⊖ If you are designing a house, arrange to have the nonsewer effluent (sinks, drains, washers, and so on) empty into an area in your garden where the plants can utilize this water instead of letting it be wasted through the sewage treatment plant.

⊖ Fight the discounts generally given to large-quantity water users. We should be discouraging large-scale use of water rather than subsidizing it.

⊖ Support measures to limit the number of people inhabiting areas with water problems, and fight proposals to ship in water from elsewhere.

Water Quality and Sewage Treatment

Sewage treatment is a process that everyone should understand but many people don't even know exists. There are several types, or levels, of sewage treatment. Each level is more expensive than the last, but also produces water of higher quality.

In some areas, individual septic tanks and cesspools are still the common means of handling sewage. This technique is quite safe and acceptable where there is low-density housing and little chance of contaminating the ground water supply. In most municipalities, however, centrally controlled sewage treatment plants are favored.

"Primary" sewage treatment involves removing grit by screening, grinding, and allowing large particles to settle out. It costs about 3.5¢ per 1,000 gallons (7). Primary treatment alone, however, does not remove the health hazards presented by bacteria, pesticides, and phosphates, and thus cannot be considered acceptable.

Secondary treatment consists of the biological removal of nutrients remaining after primary treatment. This may be accomplished with activated sludge (bacterial action) or by tricklefilters, in which water trickles over rocks occupied by microorganisms that gobble up the passing nutrients. Secondary treatment costs around 8.3¢ per 1,000 gallons (7), and produces water that may be used for agricultural and industrial purposes. The remaining sludge can be cured to make a safe fertilizer.

Even more desirable is tertiary treatment, which includes several processes that can be used in different proportions, depending upon the type of resulting water desired. These processes include reverse osmosis, electrodialysis, chlorination, irradiation (to kill harmful microbes), coagulation, and flocculation. They serve to further remove the small amount of remaining organic matter and soften the water by removing minerals. Odors and tastes can be removed by activated charcoal. Tertiary treatment costs 13–34¢ per 1,000 gallons (7), and the water produced can be used, depending upon the amount of treatment applied, as high-grade industrial water, as agriculture water for food grown for human consumption, or even as fresh, clean, drinkable water for home use.

Water is a valuable resource which we must soon begin recycling. It is estimated that by 2010 we will have barely enough water available to meet the demand (42). We can no longer afford to dispose of fresh water after a single use. The cost of making water potable compares favorably with the cost of water now being delivered to most cities from rivers and reservoirs.

Many pilot plants for tertiary treatment have been constructed and are in operation. Lake Washington, which was threatened with eutrophication, is now once again crystal-clear because of treatment that ensures that all water leaving the sewage treatment plant is clean enough for water contact sports (7). The cost of this treatment seems well worth the price.

If you would like to know more about sewage treatment and its potential for providing us once again with clear lakes and rivers, write the Super-

intendent of Documents, U.S. Government Printing
Office, Washington, D.C. 20402, for the booklet *A
Primer on Waste Water Treatment* (CWA-12, 55¢).
The December 1970 edition of National Geographic
has a very descriptive diagram of the tertiary treat-
ment plant now located at Lake Tahoe (50).

ACTION

⊖ Actively support measures designed to achieve
water quality. We shouldn't have to drink bottled water. The quality of water can be im-
proved only if the population density is de-
creased and the right people are placed in key
positions to administer our water resources.
Astronauts drink clean, safe recycled water, so
why can't the average citizen?

⊖ Visit your local water-treatment plant to learn
the specific problems of your area, what type
of water treatment your plant performs, how
efficient it is, and what you can do to make your
plant's operation easier and more effective.

⊖ Support the construction and operation of sewage treatment plants that are designed to recycle safe, potable water. The technology is available, pilot plants are operating, and we must
begin to reuse water rather than let millions
of gallons be discarded.

⊖ Support research projects designed to help us
out of our one-way water use practices.

⊖ Support local and state water pollution control
agencies by voting for clean water bonds. They
consistently need renewed help in the form of
funds, equipment, staff, and public support.

B. C.   by Johnny hart

2-19

By permission of John Hart and Field Enterprises, Inc.

⊖ Press government officials and representatives at all levels to enact and enforce legislation to minimize the pollution poured into our waters by industry. We feel that an effective criterion for purity would be for the president of each company to drink from the effluent pipes of his plant!

Metals

Recent estimates have warned that several important minerals are rapidly becoming scarce. Many of these disappearing resources are vital to industrial and scientific processes. We must exert what pressure we can to utilize these materials efficiently and to facilitate their reuse. Our world cannot afford the energy expenditure and environmental degradation necessary to extract metals that are available only as very low grade ores.

In the United States, the following metals may well be unavailable by the year 2000:

PLATINUM	ZINC	NICKEL
SILVER	LEAD	CHROMIUM
GOLD	COPPER	MANGANESE
ALUMINUM	COBALT	URANIUM
TIN	TUNGSTEN	

Of these, only aluminum, copper, cobalt, tungsten, nickel, chromium, and manganese are estimated to last past the year 2000 on a worldwide basis (20).

ACTION

⊖ Buy old metal objects rather than new ones. Sell or give away items you do not use. Don't let these critical materials become part of a sanitary landfill. Repair broken or damaged objects. It is much more reasonble to keep these items in circulation than to anticipate mining our old dumps.

⊖ Don't buy jewelry. Jewelry made from precious minerals can hardly be considered essential to survival. If you find you really need jewelry, acquire pieces no longer worn by friends and relatives, construct your own from old or broken pieces, or visit pawnshops, swap meets, and estate sales to find what you want.

⊖ Return wire coat hangers to your dry cleaners for reuse.

Food

Food is an essential commodity in every individual's life. Worldwide, food is a limiting resource, and hunger and famine are common (20). The United States does not efficiently utilize its proportion of these nutrient supplies. We have a diet built around meat products, particularly beef, and we are not making enough use of alternative protein sources such as fish, poultry, and brown rice.

Even in the United States we have a large malnutrition problem, which is apparently based upon an imbalance of food supply reaching all levels of the population (20). Individuals can act toward solving these problems by conserving food materials, sharing their supply, employing reasonable guidelines for nonwasteful, yet healthful diets, and informing others about these guidelines.

In our trips to the market we are deluged with foods that contain a myriad of food additives. Many of these additives have not been sufficiently tested for safety, and many do not have any nutritional value. These additives include coloring agents, antispoilants, antibiotics, flavoring agents (75 percent of which are synthetic), thickeners, ripeners, processers, moisteners, and nutritional supplements (39). We must strive for a balanced, wholesome diet, consisting of fresh vegetables and fruits, good meats (including fowl and fish), and whole grain products, rather than the "plastic" diet made up of soft drinks, nutritionless breads and cereals, synthetic foods, and foods doctored with chemical additives to make them look fresh.

In order to preserve our right to have plant foods to eat, we must reconsider the procedure of building housing tracts on our valuable agricultural lands. We must start thinking in terms of efficient land use and nonuse. Just think of all the land lying under parking lots, in shopping centers, beneath developments, and kept in the form of nonproductive lawns in cemeteries. To make this problem even more critical, the best soil generally ends up under these concretions.

ACTION

⊖ Grow your own vegetables and fruits. It is healthful work, it imparts a feeling for growing living things, it limits the use of pesticides, and it eliminates the need for excessive packaging and preservatives. Best of all, home-grown fruits and vegetables taste far better than store-bought.

⊖ Grow food for the body and flowers for the soul.
⊖ If you do not have a yard, plant some planter
   boxes on your window sill.
⊖ Share your garden surplus with others. With
   tender loving care (and planning) your garden
   will produce a bumper crop. Don't let it die on
   the vine!
⊖ Use vegetable skins. Most of the vitamins in
   vegetables and fruits are in the skins and should

not be wasted. Potatoes, even mashed, taste better if you scrub the skins with a brush and leave them on. If you buy vegetables at the grocery store (you can't ALWAYS grow all you need) you would be wise to wash them with a mild soap and cool water when possible to eliminate some of the oil-base insecticides clinging to them.

⊖ Avoid buying produce at stores that are so "picky" that they waste large amounts of perfectly edible plant matter in making produce look "clean" for the customer. Spots on produce normally have no effect on the taste or quality of the food. If your produce man discards even the slightest amount of trimmings, ask that he make these scraps available for use in feeding pets of the customers, such as rabbits or guinea pigs.

⊖ Diversify your diet. Our land is going to be hard-pressed to produce the quantity of beef and meat from other hoofed mammals that will be increasingly required in the American diet. Eat seafood, vegetables, and perhaps chickens or rabbits you raise yourself. Don't neglect plant sources of protein such as soybeans, peas, lentils, brown rice, and whole grains.

⊖ Don't throw away leftovers. They make terrific casseroles and lunches, or can even be added to pet foods. Vegetable liquids form a base for gourmet soups, sauces, and gravies.

⊖ When dining in a restaurant, avoid ordering more than you can eat. If you are not able to finish, ask for a "doggie bag" and have a fantastic lunch the next day. Support restaurants that recycle their scraps by giving or selling them to hogfarms or the like. Don't be embarrassed to ask. If you anticipate not finishing your dinner, bring your own doggie bag and reuse it.

Food Scraps

Don't think of the scraps left from a meal as garbage. There are much more productive ways to use nutrients in these scraps than putting them in a garbage can or down a disposal. Organic scraps present no serious problems in sewage treatment if you grind them up in your disposal, but using needless water and adding extra nutrients that may cause eutrophication should be avoided.

ACTION

- ⊖ For nutritional and tasty soup stock made from meat and vegetable food scraps, see the many wonderful recipes in *Let's Cook It Right* by Adelle Davis.
- ⊖ Use food scraps to enrich the diet of pets.
- ⊖ Take drippings obtained from cooking meats to a local meat market that will buy them and use them to make lard.
- ⊖ Make your own soap from animal fat drippings.
- ⊖ Recycle the nutrients in food scraps and put them back into the soil in the form of compost.
- ⊖ Ask if your sewage treatment plant offers free fertilizer. Sewage sludge generally takes about 30 days to "cure" at the plant into a loamy, bacteria-free, rich fertilizer. In many cities, the

HOMEMADE SOAP RECIPE (21):

1. Pour 1 cup of cold water into a container.
2. Add 5 tablespoons of lye. Be very careful to prevent spillage. Use gloves or cover hands with vaseline.
   When purchasing lye, don't buy too much at once, since it will lose its potency quickly, once opened.
3. Mix over a sink until dissolved and clear, then let it set for a few minutes.
4. Put 3 cups of any lard, animal fat, bacon drippings, or candle stubs into a blender (or if you are of a hardy nature, stir by hand).
5. Pour the lye over the fat and mix. If you are using a blender, start on low for a short time, then continue on fast speed.
6. Blend well until thickened.
7. Pour into a Pyrex cake pan or a wooden mold. Use cheesecloth or old nylons to strain the chunks out. Let it set for several days. The secret is slow setting up.
8. Cut into bars. This is best done by suspending a strong, thin wire between two sticks and pulling this through the soap.
9. Store in airtight containers.
   The soap made in this fashion can be used as hand soap or can be flaked for use in dishwashing and laundry.
   If you become proficient in the above techniques, then you can get a bit fancier and add accessory ingredients to make your soap softer, more colorful, and sweetly scented. Ingredients such as glycerine and alcohol, vegetable coloring powders, and essential oil perfumes will do the job when added during the melted stage in preparation of soaps.

COMPOSTING

Compost is the basic tool of organic gardening, and is the natural step in the biological cycle between dead or unused organic matter and growing plants. It returns to the ground the nutrients removed during plant growth and maintains the tilth of the soil. Compost is the most complete and revitalizing and the least expensive form of soil additive a garden can receive.

The production of compost is very easy and can be carried out on various levels of sophistication and time-space-energy requirements. The simplest approach to composting is the *heap*. One simply piles, preferably in layers, straw, weeds, or lawn clippings; manure and pet deposits; kitchen refuse (organic); seaweed (preferably with the salt washed off); and any other organic material he comes by.

The *bin* is preferable to the heap because it keeps out dogs and provides better exposure of the decaying materials to air. This means that both aerobic and anaerobic bacteria can be at work, causing faster decomposition and eliminating any odors. (If a layer of grass clippings and/or soil is kept on the top of the pile and odoriferous materials are sunk in below this layer, odor isn't much of a problem anyway.) Compost bins can easily be constructed of rocks, stones, or broken bricks, leaving spaces for air to enter (22). Or you can simply sink four corner posts and stretch picket fencing or poultry wire around them to form the sides. You may want to construct a more elaborate wooden bin with slotted sides, including perhaps a drainage system whereby you can retrieve water which has percolated down through the pile. This "compost water" is useful for treating sick plants or encouraging young ones to grow faster. If you have very limited yard space, you may want to try a round, metal container that can be partially buried in the ground (e.g., the Bard-Matic Garbage Eliminator (22) or a rusty metal garbage can). Household vegetable and meat wastes put into this container will provide humus for potted plants and window boxes.

The amount of time it takes to produce compost, or humus, by any of these methods varies with moisture, season, and the types of materials present in the pile. Usually the compost is ready in three to six months. Addition of such materials as kitchen scraps, pet wastes, and manure speeds up decomposition because of their relatively high nitrogen content. Occasional turning of the pile also speeds decomposition. The compost pile should be kept about as moist as a damp sponge, which means uncovering it in wet weather and watering and covering it in very dry weather.

The smaller the size of the particles of organic matter put in the pile, the faster they will decompose. Therefore, a community shredder that can be used by many families is a great help. However, running a rotary lawnmower over small branches and other fibrous materials works fairly well. Place the material to be shredded near a wall so it can be easily retrieved.

Plastic bags of the type sold for lining trash cans can be used as mini-compost bins. Material to be composted should be moistened slightly and put in the bag. Then close the bag, fasten the top, and place it in a shady spot. In warm weather, humus should be ready in a few weeks, and the bag can be filled with new material for composting.

parks department will have first chance at this fertilizer, but the public can use whatever is left. Bring your own container and be sure to call the plant before going since the availability depends upon the curing time and the approval of the health department. In some parts of the country, especially around the Great Lakes, much of this fertilizer is packaged and sold to the public, thereby repaying some of the cost of sewage treatment.

Endangered Wildlife

Much of our wildlife, including both plants and animals, is becoming quite rare. Redwoods are endangered by man's highways and habitations, and plant species that live only on sand dunes are being destroyed by recreational vehicles (10).

Any fool can destroy trees, they cannot defend themselves or run away.—John Muir

Many wild animals, particularly the predator species, are approaching extinction. As a result, rodent and ungulate populations are booming and we are being robbed of the unique experience of seeing many beautifully adapted creatures in the wild. The Department of the Interior, Washington, D.C., now lists 101 species of endangered animals. Obtain the list of these endangered species from them or from your congressman. With the help of your natural history museum or department of fish and game, determine which ones your way of life may affect.

By permission of John Hart and Field Enterprises, Inc.

ACTION

⊖ Support all our endangered species. Not only don't hunt them, but don't allow their habitats to be destroyed for the building of housing tracts, dams, highways, or man's other encroachments. Remember that all of our technology cannot replace a species that has become extinct.

⊖ Don't buy garments made of the furs or skins of wild animals. Point out to those who would acquire status by wearing the pelts of exotic species that all of these animals are now rare and are fast disappearing. Use only hides of animals that have been slaughtered for meat, or of those that are raised for their fur (mink, chinchilla, rabbits, and so on), or use synthetics that look and feel like fur.

⊖ Social pressure is having a marked effect. Some unions that deal with furs have refused to transport or cut skins of certain rare species (30). California has passed a law forbidding the importation for sale of skins, hides, and other parts of several endangered species. Encourage such action where you live.

⊖ Help eliminate bounties on large predators. Bounties are at least partially responsible for the decline of such animals as cougars and bobcats. Other animals like prairie dogs and mustangs should be protected from the wanton poisoning and shooting programs that threaten to eliminate them.

⊖ Read the labels of pet foods and cosmetics; don't buy them if they contain whale products.

Our precious whales are being slaughtered to provide meat for pet foods and oil for cosmetics, both of which can easily be made without any whale material at all. Write letters of protest to manufacturers who use whale products. If you wish to support the effort to have our whales effectively protected by international law, you can contribute to the WHALE FUND of the New York Zoological Society, Bronx Zoo, New York, N.Y. 10460. Contributions are tax-deductible.

Land

Each year one million acres of land are converted from agricultural use to such urban uses as housing development, airports, highways, reservoirs, and flood control projects (2). This means that about 2,740 acres per day of agricultural land are being consumed for other uses! These frightening facts point out the necessity for closely scrutinizing our present land use policies.

The President's Council on Environmental Quality sums up this problem by saying, "Land use is still not guided by any agreed-upon standards. It is instead influenced by a welter of sometimes competing, overlapping governmental institutions and programs, private and public attitudes and biases, and distorted economic incentives"(2).

Historically, Americans have striven to "tame the wilderness," thus justifying the thoughtless, indiscriminate development of our valuable agricultural and wilderness areas. We are now discovering that many of the resulting human environments have created more problems than they have solved. Three fourths of all Americans now live in urban environments and have become estranged from the land. Adapting to life in a ghetto is something that no human being should have to do. Plans must be developed, using quality of life as the primary criterion, that will insure optimum human density and environmental health.

Every time we hear the phrase "progress is inevitable," we must question its validity. We do not have to sit by and watch speculators and greedy developers gobble up our open spaces. The promised economic benefits of increased development materialize only up to a point. After the optimum size is reached, the increased problems and social complexities cause the cost per individual to rise.

Economic costs are not the only concern; social costs, including congestion, noise, air and water pollution, crime, and disorder are equally important (41). Social costs increase, not directly with population increase, but rather as the *square* of population size. Therefore, the larger the "tax base" (taxpayers, houses, and industries), the greater the taxes and social costs each individual must pay.

Some localities now understand the problem. Santa Clara County, California, is reported to be reconsidering its policy of attracting new industry and more people. According to one of their supervisors, "We've come to the realization that growth for growth's sake is no longer desirable." The county was promised more jobs and more taxpayers, but it got environmental problems such as traffic congestion, air pollution, ugly landscapes, and noise instead. New jobs generally went to outsiders, because local people were trained more for agricultural occupations than for the new industrial jobs. The local people did, however, receive more than their share of real estate agents. They also found that the new residents didn't pay enough taxes to support what they required in the form of new streets, street improvements, schools, fire protection, and police protection (40).

Freeways are an excellent example of a misplaced priority on land use. Highway right-of-way often consumes flat agricultural land or public lands, which are relatively inexpensive to acquire (51). Freeway expansion encourages increased use of automobiles, producing a host of negative effects. More petroleum products are consumed and more air pollution is produced. More service facilities and shopping centers spring up along the roadways, and billboards quickly exploit the newly opened habitat.

Freeways, like other paved areas, rob the water table of much of its natural replenishment by rain water. The water falling on pavement is drained off into storm sewers, never having an opportunity to soak into the soil.

Many of our highways actually do much to destroy natural beauty and the habitats of plants and animals that contributed much of the aesthetic value that created public demand for the roadway in the first place. Sometimes the preservation of endangered species of animals and plants, and of certain types of wild lands, may require that no highways at all be constructed into certain areas.

Highway programs should be integrated into total planning programs at Federal, regional, and community levels to help eliminate patchwork paving of the landscape. The emphasis should be on planning the most efficient use with the least amount of paving. This involves acquisition of right-of-way on the basis of environmental, rather than strictly economic, cost. It also presupposes that plans for many proposed highways will be scrapped, and the money and planning will be channeled into the development of fast, efficient, and usable systems of mass transit.

Estuaries, sloughs, and other coastal wetlands have proved to be prime targets for the developer's bulldozers. These wetlands support vast numbers of fish, birds, mammals, and plants. However, these areas exist in pleasant, seaside locations and few birds and fish are registered voters! For this reason, more than 80 percent of all wetlands in California are now replaced with marinas, hotels, houses, and popcorn stands (52).

ACTION

⊖ Question every new development or building program in your locale as to its environmental consequences and real economic and social impact. We should be more concerned for the land than for the pocketbooks of developers.

⊖ Landowners cannot be allowed to do anything they want with their land. Consideration of the surrounding populace and landscape should be foremost. Adherence to this principle will help alleviate some of the destructive operations of individual developers and strengthen community spirit in determining the course of future development.

⊖ Create and enforce a general plan for your community. Without an idea of what direction development must take to satisfy the community's economic and environmental needs, disorganized and detrimental outward expansion will soon destroy the potential of the region to achieve a healthful accord of man and nature.

⊖ Support the strengthening of planning laws. A general plan can be effective only if it is strongly enforced. Zoning land is a relatively weak way to protect it. Zoning changes are too commonly approved by the very people who planned them to protect certain areas. We need an informed, active public to ensure that the zoning rules we have are doing their job and that protective zoning is maintained. The referendum is a powerful tool by which the people may remind local officials that they want to adhere to the general plan and not allow detrimental variances.

⊖ Reorganize taxes so that agricultural land will not be so susceptible to development. If our farm lands were not taxed out of existence, there would be less loss of these valuable, food-producing open spaces.

⊖ Federal activities such as building dams, plants, and military bases can have a large impact on an area and may attract thousands of new occupants (2). Before encouraging and allowing Federal construction in your area, consider the impact of these extra people. Projects planned by Federal agencies can now be challenged in the courts (42).

⊖ The question is always asked, "But where will all these people go, if they can't come here?" Each community has to decide upon its own optimum size and density. Once an area is sufficiently populated, subsequent increase mean an imposition upon the present occupants and should be avoided. The ultimate solutions are to stem population growth and to distribute efficiently the people we already have.

⊖ Declare war on signs. There is nothing uglier or more depressing than a whole series of garish, flashing signs along a roadway. Many cities have initiated sign ordinances that limit the size and use of advertising signs and billboards. For ideas regarding ways to limit sign use, write for the booklet from the California Roadside Council, 2636 Ocean Avenue, San Francisco, Calif. 94132.

Consumer Power

Having emphasized the detrimental effects of many of our consuming habits, we would now like to illustrate the channels by which we can use our power as consumers, or nonconsumers, to bring about needed changes in the quality and quantity of the goods we buy. The aim of consumer power is to eliminate wastage.

Concern for environmental health and quality of life produces a fresh view of the aims and methods of advertising. Too often, advertising seeks to cajole us into buying items we certainly don't need and might not even want (they call it "opening new markets"). We are made to feel that we will become outcasts if we don't stay in fashion and that we must continually buy items that will indicate our rising status. It is up to us to indicate to advertisers that, whereas we are interested in being informed about good products, we see through the sham of fashion, status, and created "needs."

ACTION

⊖ Buy clothes and other goods that will be useful for a long time, not those that are associated with a fad that will soon disappear. Buy durable shoes and clothing and wear them out.

⊖ Don't throw away items you no longer use. Give them directly to people who can use them, or donate them to groups or organizations that will

70

see that they reach potential users. The Salvation Army and Goodwill Industries accept repairable items, which they return to usefulness. There are sure to be other organizations in your area that can channel goods to those who can use them.

⊖ Refuse to shop at stores that give trading stamps, for they simply encourage people to consume items they often really don't need, just to use up the stamps. They also increase the price of every item in the store. If you already have some trading stamps, consider turning them in for a cash refund rather than getting an item you don't really want.

⊖ Buy used articles whenever they will serve the purpose, rather than supporting the trend to acquire new things continually. This includes clothes, cars, appliances, and recreational equipment. Demanding durable items and buying old, good ones rather than newer ones with built-in obsolescence can help persuade manufacturers to produce higher quality, longer-lasting products. Planned obsolescence is widespread in this country because it is profitable. We can put a stop to it by making it unprofitable!

⊖ If you have bought an item and find that the claims that induced you to buy it were misleading, that it was poorly constructed, or that it was actually designed to cease functioning after a short time, take definite and immediate action. (1) First, inform the manufacturer of your displeasure with his product. Be very specific about your complaints. (2) Send another copy to the President's Assistant on Consumer

Affairs, presently Mrs. Virginia Knauer, in the Executive Offices, The White House, Washington, D.C. 20025. (3) Third, and very important, *tell your friends.* Word of mouth is still the most effective means of advertising—pro or con.

⊖ Organize boycotts against products that are dangerous, wasteful, or fraudulently advertised. This often is a very effective way of pointing out the faults of these products to manufacturers and potential buyers alike.

⊖ Avoid being caught up in the skyrocketing consumption associated with holiday periods.

⊖ When selecting holiday gifts, be sure to choose items that you know the recipient needs and will use. Especially avoid the small electrical appliance gift cop-out.

⊖ Suggest to friends and acquaintances that you exchange warm good wishes rather than token gifts. They will probably be pleased and relieved.

⊖ Make gifts yourself. This expresses a much greater investment of time and thought than buying them. You can also recycle many items by using them in gift-making.

⊖ Refer to STATIONERY, CARDS, AND WRAPPINGS for gift-wrapping hints.

⊖ Cranberry and popcorn strings, pine cones, decorated cookies and gingerbread men, pomander fruits, and popcorn balls make beautiful decorations, and do not provide the waste problems of tinsel, Styrofoam, and breakable glass ornaments.

Pollutants

Pesticides

A great deal of poison is released into the environment through the use of pesticides. Many of these poisons are extremely hazardous, both to you and to the environment. Remember, chemical companies are in the business of selling pesticides. They are not overzealous in advertising the present or potential drawbacks of their products. It is important to know the kinds of compounds that are used as insecticides and the specific dangers inherent in their use, so that our action in this area can be selective and effective.

There are several general drawbacks to pesticides.

Immunity. Insects can rapidly develop immunities to pesticides. If only a few insects out of millions are not killed by the poison, their offspring will probably be resistant also. This is the reason that DDT, although initially very toxic to houseflies and mosquitoes, is now virtually harmless to many of them.

Loss of Beneficial Insects. Many insecticides are wide-spectrum poisons, or biocides. That is, they kill many different kinds of organisms, both good and bad, often destroying the checks and balances of the natural system in the area. Large population explosions of pests may result when the beneficial predatory insects are inadvertently killed by pesticides.

By permission of John Hart and Field Enterprises, Inc.

Residues. Some insecticides are extremely long lasting and, moreover, are very hard to remove once applied. Experiments conducted with malathion, a commonly used insecticide on citrus fruits, gooseberries, plums, tomatoes, apples, and stringbeans showed that no malathion was lost when the fruit was stored under refrigeration for up to eight months. Washing in running water for one minute sometimes removed NONE of the residue (33).

For these reasons, and for others still to be discussed, the use of insecticides should be reduced to an absolute minimum. However, if use of an insecticide is indicated, the following information will suggest which pesticides should be strictly avoided and which might be less harmful and particularly applicable to the pest problem at hand.

There are several types, or classes, of insecticides.

Botanicals are short-lived poisons extracted from plants. They quickly break down into harmless compounds, and do not leave harmful residues in the environment as many synthetic insecticides do. Also, the botanicals tend to be somewhat specific to soft-bodied insects such as aphids, thrips, caterpillars, and so on. There is thus less danger of harm to beneficial insects, such as ladybugs and wasps, and other animals of all sorts.

Synthetic organic insecticides are the most heavily used insecticides. All are potentially dangerous and the use of some creates extremely serious problems. Three groups of this type of insecticide are commonly used.

Chlorinated hydrocarbons are often extremely *long-lived.* Their permanence has been one of the primary reasons for their success, but it is also their great drawback. Because they do not break down readily, they tend to remain in the environment far longer than intended. Carried by water and air far from their original site of use, they can find their way through food and drink into the bodies of many organisms, where they may remain for years. All kinds of animals ranging from crabs to trout to deer can be injured or killed by chlorinated hydro-carbons (33). Some can kill birds in great numbers outright, or can cause them to lay eggs with shells so thin they crack after being laid (20). The effects of these chemicals on man are not completely known. However, cardiac and respiratory failures leading to death have been reported from acute poisoning by some of these insecticides (34).

Organophosphates are insecticides in the same class of chemical compounds as many of the nerve gases. Like nerve gas, they cause muscle paralysis and eventual death (35). While they are *highly dangerous*, they are normally much less persistent than many of the chlorinated hydrocarbons. "No-Pest" strips and flea collars (DDVP or Dichloros Vapona®) both produce organophosphate vapors, and both have proved toxicity to human beings and pets (36).

Organophosphates are often very-wide-spectrum toxins, killing many animals other than the pests for which they are intended (37). The number of human fatalities directly attributable to some of these compounds is growing. Organophosphates should be used only with extreme care, by a person aware of their dangers.

Carbamates apparently act in much the same way as the organophosphates. In general, they are not as harmful to mammals as the organophosphates, but there are exceptions.

The selection of a carbamate must be made with extreme care. The different types of carbamates have quite different effects on animals. Carbaryl, for instance, is relatively harmless to mammals, but is extremely toxic to honeybees. Zectran is deadly to mammals, but is fairly harmless to insects like honeybees (38).

ACTION

⊖ Cut down NOW on the pesticides you are using, and urge your friends and neighbors to do the same. One point to emphasize is that you do not need to use most of these substances to have a healthy, productive garden and an attractive, well-kept landscape. If you have a gardener, be sure he understands the importance of cutting down pesticide use.

⊖ Grow those types of plants that are the most resistant to pests and disease. When selecting which fruits and vegetables to grow, check in seed catalogs or with your nurseryman for the types that are best for your area in terms of growing ability and pest- and disease-resistance.

⊖ For ornamental and other landscaping needs, try using plants that are native to your area. They are already tolerant to many pests in your region and generally need less care.

⊖ Certain plants like marigolds, painted daisies, garlic, and many other herbs are repellent to insects. These may be very helpful when sprinkled among other plants or grown in borders around them.

⊖ A diversified assemblage of plants can be the key to a healthy landscape and garden. If many types of plants are grown, a small number of different pests are less likely to do much harm. Do not retain one type of plant that obviously requires more upkeep and care than it is worth.

⊖ Isolate and destroy any diseased or insect-ridden plants. This in itself may be sufficient to stop the infestation.

⊖ Blast water from the hose on affected plants to remove such things as aphids, leafhoppers, and spittlebugs. An application of slightly soapy water (not detergent) is also very effective against aphids, as it dries them out.

⊖ Natural predators, such as birds, ladybugs, and lacewings can be very effective against aphids, caterpillars, and oak moths. Beneficial insects can be obtained from many suppliers, several of whom advertise in *Organic Gardening and Farming Magazine*. It may be worthwhile to check with your local agricultural agent for suppliers in your area. Some pest control companies are knowledgeable about recently developed techniques that can safely eliminate household and garden pests.

⊖ Encourage lizards, toads, salamanders, and non-poisonous snakes and spiders to live in your garden by providing hiding places for them under shingles or rocks. Above all, don't kill them or drive them away. These valuable predators are voracious eaters of a variety of garden pests, and are true allies to any gardener.

⊖ The mosquitofish, *Gambusia affinis,* is a predator that is often effective in cutting down mosquito populations. Your local Mosquito Abate-
ment Commission can often supply these fish,
or they may be netted from local streams and
brooks which have already been stocked with
them. If the fish are not available, spray mosquito breeding grounds with light oil or kero-
sene, which cuts the larvae off from air. This
oil is far less toxic than any insecticide. Pyreth-
rin sprays should be used only if other methods
have failed. Don't allow water to stand in bird-
baths, barrels, pots, and cans that might serve
as mosquito breeding grounds.

⊖ Spray deciduous trees and shrubs with inert
oil and mineral compounds in the winter when
they are leafless and dormant. These sprays
smother eggs and adults of mites, scale, spittlebugs, and whiteflies, and they are not poisonous.

⊖ Snails can be eliminated in several ways. Perhaps the best method is to water plants at
sundown, then come out after dark with a
flashlight and kill the browsing snails. Beer or
vinegar, placed in shallow pans at ground level,
is reputed to kill snails and slugs. If baits seem
appropriate, use one which contains only metal-
dehyde (no arsenic) and place it in small pans
to keep it out of the soil. After clearing an
area of snails, block off further access by placing a line of sawdust, silica aquagel, or diatoma-
ceous earth around the plants.

⊖ Eliminate flies with flyswatters and fly paper,
or keep them out with screen doors.

⊖ Use ant stakes to control ants. They contain

arsenic, so be sure that the poison never touches the ground and that they are kept safely away from children and pets.

⊖ Refer to the *Encyclopedia of Organic Gardening* (*see* BOOKS) for further information on specific, nonpesticide treatments.

⊖ If you must use pesticides, keep applications to a minimum. Use them only on those areas affected by the pest. Never use them as a preventative measure. Use hand-pump sprayers rather than hose-end ones, which put out too much spray too fast. Use powder rather than liquid when possible.

⊖ Find out what pesticides the city park, school, and highway maintenance departments are employing. If they are using toxic or persistent compounds, bring this fact to public attention and urge or force them to use less dangerous substances or none at all.

⊖ Never use one-package mixtures composed of fertilizer, weed killer, and insecticide.

⊖ Be extremely cautious about believing the claims of chemical companies about the safety of pesticides. It is very difficult to test the toxicity of these compounds accurately. The pesticides may come in contact with many animals, and no testing program can determine the effects of a chemical on all exposed animals. Furthermore, it is almost impossible to test the long-term effects of certain pesticides, simply because many of them have not been around long enough for the long-term effects to become evident.

⊖ Know the ingredients of the product you are

considering. If there is no list of ingredients on the pesticide container, or if only technical names of the chemicals are listed, the manufacturer may have a reason for not wanting you to know what is in it. DO NOT BUY IT!

⊖ Pesticides are poisons, and extreme care should always be taken in selecting the correct one. The following list can be used to determine what ingredients and compounds should be completely avoided, and which are ecologically more acceptable for certain uses.

⊖ Use *botanicals*, which are generally the least dangerous to the environment of all the insecticides. Botanicals include

Dimethrin	Rotenone
Nicotine	Ryania
Pyrethrins	Sabadilla
Pyrethrum	

Nicotine can be obtained by soaking cigarette butts or pipe tobacco in water, then spraying or sprinkling the resulting solution on the affected plants.

⊖ Use of *chlorinated hydrocarbons* should be entirely avoided. A report published in 1969 by the Department of Health, Education, and Welfare recommended a complete halt to the use of DDT and DDD and stringent restraints on the use of all other chlorinated hydrocarbons. All of us should stop using these chemicals now, thus helping to end this source of poisoning of our environment.

The following list gives the names of many of the chlorinated hydrocarbons often sold in commercial insecticides. We suggest you register a complaint with the dealer selling products containing these compounds, communicate your displeasure to the manufacturer, and support legislation banning these long-lived poisons.

Acaraben (Chloro-
    benzilate)
Acaralate (Chloro-
    propylate)

Aldrin
Bandane
Chlordane
DDD

	Leaf Chewers							Sucking Insects							
	beetles	weevils	caterpillars	earwigs	grasshoppers	oak moths	snails, slugs	aphids	leafhoppers	mealybugs	scale	spider mites	spittlebugs	thrips	whiteflies
Pyrethrum			X					X	X					X	
Rotenone (cube)	X		X					X	X					X	
Di-syston (granules)								X	X		X	X	X	X	X
Meta-systox-R								X	X	X	X	X	X	X	X
Cygon (Dimethoate)								X	X	X	X	X		X	X
Sevin (Carbaryl)	X	X	X	X	X	X		X	X		X		X	X	X
Malathion	X	X		X	X			X	X	X	X		X	X	X
Guthion			X		X			X	X	X	X	X	X	X	X
Dibrom			X	X	X	X		X	X	X	X	X	X	X	X
Diazinon	X	X	X	X	X			X	X	X	X	X	X	X	X
Metaldehyde							X								
Petroleum oils								X		X	X	X			X
Sodium fluosilicate				X											
Ethylene dichloride															
Dichloroethyl ether															

Chart of Acceptable

DDT
Dieldrin
Dimite
Dizane
Endosulfan (Thiodan)
Endrin
Heptachlor
Kelthane (Dicofol)

Lindane (Benzene hexachloride)
Ovex
Pentachloronitrobenzene
Tetradifon (Tedion)
Tothane (TDE)
Toxaphene

⊖ *Organophosphates* are generally more toxic

Soil Pests						Burrowers				Nuisance Insects							
cutworms	grubs	lawn moths	soil mealybugs	symphylids	wireworms	codling moths	leaf miners	corn earworms	borers	ants	houseflies	mosquitoes	yellowjackets	wasps	hornets	bedbugs, fleas	cockroaches, silverfish
		X									X	X					
		X						X			X	X	X	X	X		
						X											
			X			X											
				X		X					X						
X	X	X		X		X		X	X								
								X		X		X				X	X
						X											
X		X						X		X	X	X					
X	X	X	X	X	X	X	X		X	X	X	X				X	X
									X								
X	X	X	X														

Pesticide Uses

than the botanicals but tend to be shorter-lived than the chlorinated hydrocarbons. Use with extreme care!

Abate	Malathion
Baytex (Fenthion)	Meta-Systox-R (Oxy-
Co-Ral (Coumaphos)	demetomethyl)
Cygen (Dimethoate)	Parathion
Diazinon	Phosdrin
Dibrom (Naled)	(Mevinphos)
Dursban	Systox (Demeton)
Guthion (Azinphos-	Vapona (Dichloros,
methyl)	DDVP)

There are alternatives to flea collars, which contain DDVP. One product, sold under the name "Dry-Die," contains only pyrethrins and nonpoisonous silica gel powder. Consult your veterinarian for the safest way to keep your pet free of fleas.

⊖ *Carbamates* should be used with generally the same care as the organophosphates and use of specific kinds should be directed at specific pests.

Baygon	Lannate (Methomyl)
Bux-10	Sevin (Carbaryl)
Furadan (Carbofuran)	Zectran

Herbicides

The use of weed killers should be severely limited. There is considerable evidence that some widely used poisons, such as 2,4,5-T and 2,4-D, are toxic to nonpest plants and animals, including human beings (54). These compounds should be avoided and alternatives employed whenever possible.

ACTION

⊖ Uproot unwanted plants. Conquering weeds by your own efforts can be a rewarding and pleasurable experience.

⊖ Mulching can be of benefit in combating weeds. By spreading sawdust, straw, leaves, newspaper (in strips, shredded, or whole), and other organic materials on the soil, moisture is retained and weed growth retarded.

⊖ If you must use an herbicide, use only as much as you need, and use it with extreme care. These chemicals are poisons and should be treated as such.

Cleansers

"It is more important to save our lakes than to get our shirts whiter than white." This is the conclusion of a House committee after a thorough investigation of the environmental effects of detergents and their additives (29).

This same committee described detergents as "cleansers, which cut grease and suspend dirt." Included are soap and synthetic detergents. In popular usage, the term detergent is restricted to the synthetics. Besides the detergent component, commercial products usually contain one or more "builders" to improve performance.

Soaps and detergents clean by attaching themselves to dirt, grease, or other particles, making these particles water-soluble so that they lift off of the surface of the article being washed. The minerals occurring in high concentrations in "hard" water tie up the soap or detergent molecules, blocking their ability to attach to dirt particles. Detergent manufacturers add phosphates to their products to take the troublesome minerals out of action.

When phosphates are dumped into bodies of water from sewage outfalls, they can contribute to the process of eutrophication, thus accelerating the aging of lakes. This aging process would normally take thousands of years but now takes only tens of years in eutrophied lakes. Phosphates can stimulate the growth of tremendous quantities of algae. When this plant life dies, its decomposition robs the water of much of its oxygen and produces poisonous hydrogen sulfide gas, killing fish and much other aquatic life. Eventually, the lake fills in with decayed matter and becomes marshy.

Detergents contribute approximately 50 percent of the phosphates that are dumped into our waters (2). A second source of phosphates is the runoff from fertilizers used on land. Nitrogen can play a role in eutrophication similar to that played by phosphates, and its sources are essentially the same.

Most heavy-duty detergents contain at least 50 percent phosphates, and enzyme presoaks contain up to 80 percent. The search is on for substitutes for these phosphates, and there are some potential replacements. Nitrilotriacetic acid (NTA) was considered a likely one—but it is being phased out. Conversion to NTA would have yielded more problems than it solved. It contains nitrogen (also a plant nutrient), it may be toxic in certain forms, and it "locks up" metals, thus possibly damaging plumbing and presenting heavy metal pollution problems in lake sediments. The use of polyelectrolytes is being investigated as an alternative to phosphates (31).

The Soap and Detergent Association announced in December 1970 that all major brands of detergents (laundry and dishwashing) will include on their labels the phosphorus content and the number of grams of phosphate per recommended "dose." If this does come true, check carefully the detergent that you use.

Several ingredients of detergents have recently come under attack for their alleged dangers. It has been found that high amounts of arsenic are contained in the phosphates used in detergents. Whether or not this presents a health hazard is being debated (31, 44, 47). The enzymes now common in many detergents are under scrutiny because they cause skin rashes (45, 46).

All soaps and almost all the detergents sold for household use in the last few years degrade rather rapidly. The term biodegradability refers to the ability of substances to be broken down by organisms. The important factor is the rate at which this process occurs. In 1965, the detergent industry changed to chemicals that would break down more easily, thereby virtually eliminating the problem of foam produced by laundry detergents (42). Some hard or nondegradable detergents are still being

PHOSPHATE CONTENT OF MAJOR DETERGENTS
(Courtesy of Federal Water Quality Administration)

Laundry Detergents

COLDWATER ALL LIQUID	less than 1%
WHITE KING SOAP	less than 1%
LUX LIQUID	1.9%
IVORY LIQUID	1.9%
ADDIT LIQUID	2.2%
PAR PLUS	4.3%
WISK LIQUID	14.2%
INSTANT FEL SOAP	16.6%
ROYALITE	21.7%
WHITE KING WITH BORAX	34.7%
FAB	34.8%
CHEER	36.3%
BREEZE	37.2%
BONUS	37.5%
BESTLINE B-7	38.0%
DUZ	38.3%
GAIN	39.5%
RINSO WITH CHLORINE BLEACH	41.0%
DREFT	41.9%
PUNCH	44.2%
COLD POWER	44.6%
AJAX LAUNDRY	44.6%
COLD WATER ALL POWDER	45.4%
BOLD	45.4%
OXYDOL	46.6%
DRIVE	47.4%
COLDWATER SURF	48.2%
AMWAY SA-8	49.3%
TIDE	49.8%

contributed by industrial effluents, however. Thus, biodegradability is a common quality of commercially sold soaps and detergents, but a product that

(Continued)

SALVO   56.6%
BLUE RAIN DROPS   63.2%

Presoaks

AXION   63.2%
AMWAY TRIZYME   71.2%
ENZYME BRION   71.4%
BIZ   73.9%

Automatic Dishwasher Detergents

ELECTROSOL   34.8%
CALGONITE   49.4%
ALL   54.0%
CASCADE   54.5%
AMWAY   60.0%

---

is biodegradable may still contribute, in other ways, to serious environmental problems.

ACTION

⊖ Check the accompanying chart of phosphate contents of the major detergent brands for your detergent. It is the amount of phosphate per washload that is important. If your brand contains a large amount of phosphate, consider switching to one with a smaller amount (or none!).

⊖ Certain products that are relatively safe ecologically are not listed in this chart. Some of these have been tested by other sources and are low in phosphate. The following products are available only from distributors: Shaklee Products, Hayward, Calif. 94544; Amway Corporation, Ada, Mich. 49301; Bestline Products, Box 6146, San Jose, Calif. 95150. Write or call these companies (most are listed in the telephone book) about their products and use those that you have determined to be safe.

⊖ Support those companies that are now making safe products. Both Sears Roebuck and Co. and Montgomery Ward have recently come out with nonphosphate detergents that are purported to clean as well as those already on the market.

⊖ Liquids for washing dishes by hand, some bleaches, and household cleaners contain little or no phosphates and therefore present no eutrophication problems. However, chlorine bleaches and cleansers can kill the helpful bacteria that break down the grease that can clog your pipes. To keep your plumbing clear, investigate the use of dried bacterial cultures that are now being sold in many hardware stores across the country. For specific information contact Gerald C. Bower, Inc., 1139 West Struck Avenue, Orange, Calif. 92667. Another solution for clogged drains is washing soda. The instructions are on the package.

⊖ Use laundry soaps such as Duz Soap, Ivory Snow, Ivory Flakes, Lux Flakes, or Maple Leaf Flakes instead of detergents. Add washing soda or borax to the load if your area has hard water.

⊖ Urge detergent manufacturers to vary the amount of water softeners (such as phosphates or their equivalent) with the hardness of the water in the area in which the detergent is being sold. To sell detergents with high phosphates in an area with soft water is wasteful. If you are interested in finding out the hardness of your water, contact your water department or write for the pamphlet *Phosphates in Detergents and the Eutrophication of America's Waters*. (House Report No. 91-1004, 40¢ from the U.S. Government Printing Office, Washington, D.C. 20402.)

⊖ Stop using enzyme presoaks. They are generally two thirds phosphate.

⊖ Prod the detergent manufacturers into stopping the use of phosphates altogether. Their worn-out answer that it cannot be done is false. Some companies have been putting out nonphosphate cleaners for years.

⊖ Whenever possible, support measures that improve sewage treatment facilities. One answer to the problem of phosphates (the one most actively supported by the Soap and Detergent Association) is to upgrade ALL our sewage treatment plants so that they eliminate phosphates. There are dried bacterial cultures that can do this job but the feasibility of converting all plants to this procedure is still uncertain. It would be an expensive job but is something to work toward.

⊖ Write your legislators asking that detergents

with phosphates be banned in your area. Some communities have already taken this step with success.

Metallic Toxins

Lead

Public attention has recently been focused on the immediate and future dangers of lead pollution. The prime source of lead contamination is tetraethyl lead, the octane-booster used in gasoline (25). After leaving the auto exhaust system, much of the lead remains in aerosol form in the air and may be carried by air currents over long distances. In the state of California alone, 50 million pounds of lead a year are being spewed out by automobiles (26). Furthermore, the increasing numbers of cars with larger, high-compression engines have produced an increase of 5 percent in lead emissions each year from 1966 through 1969 (27).

These long-term increases in atmospheric lead reportedly will result in higher concentrations in the blood of exposed populations (28). These higher concentrations increase the danger of actually getting lead poisoning when one is exposed to additional environmental sources of lead.

It is estimated that 400,000 American children between the ages of one and six may have dangerously high levels of lead in their blood (28). Much of this is contributed by flaking exterior paint and caulking compound found on window sills or frames. Whereas lead is no longer used in interior paint, it is found in exterior paints and in wall paint of pre-World War II housing, especially in slum areas.

Recently, the clay and glazes used in some Mexican and other handmade pottery have been implicated in a few cases of lead poisoning.

Lead poisoning in human beings can cause debility, lead lines around the gums, nervousness, nausea, insanity, and death.

ACTION

⊖ Drive less!
⊖ Drive a car with a low-compression engine, thereby allowing the use of the unleaded and

low-lead gasolines that are now readily available at gas stations.

⊖ Support legislation to "get the lead out" soon.

⊖ Avoid subtle potential sources of lead poisoning: lead-based paints and glazes, lead toys, lead utensils, battery parts, and so on. If you melt lead to make weights, sinkers, and such, be extremely careful, and do the work in a well-ventilated place.

⊖ Avoid using leaded gasoline as a solvent. Use white gas instead.

Mercury

Mercury poisoning can cause death, chromosome damage, and birth defects. It enters waterways from mines, agriculture, and industrial wastes in the form of inorganic mercury or phenyl mercury and settles to the bottom. It becomes transformed to methyl mercury, which is soluble in water and can enter aquatic organisms directly through the skin or by ingestion. It does not break down and accumulates as these organisms are consumed by larger animals. The mercury levels found in fish have caused 111 persons in Minamata, Japan, to be killed or seriously damaged neurologically in a span of only seven years. Nineteen of those affected were congenitally defective babies (23).

Methyl mercury used as a seed treatment to prevent fungus growth has caused drastic decreases in bird populations in Sweden, and has been implicated in the decline of America's National Bird, the bald eagle.

The threat of mercury poisoning in this country is serious. Five to ten thousand tons of mercury are lost by agricultural and industrial processes each year (23). A Federal Water Quality Administration official has estimated that 10 percent of United States waters may be endangered or spoiled for commercial and sports fishing for years or decades to come. To make matters worse, there are no known means of removing the mercury (24).

ACTION

⊖ Don't buy seeds that have been treated with mercury. W. Atlee Burpee Co., for example, has ceased to use mercury on most of their seeds, but they do use a chlorinated hydrocarbon treatment. If you cannot find information about seed treatment on the package or from your supplier, write to the companies and ask.

⊖ Support legislation to regulate the use of mercury and the dumping of wastes from quicksilver mines.

⊖ Expose local industries that discharge mercury as a waste product and urge legislation to prevent such pollution.

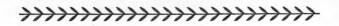

Political Action

It is apparent that polluters respond slowly or not at all to *requests* that they cease their damaging activities. Only through individuals and groups working in the political arena can we hope to stimulate immediate response.

ACTION

⊖ Know exactly how your legislators vote on environmental bills. Do not be taken in by a sudden burst of environmental awareness on the part of your representative a month before the election. Check the person's voting record. Organizations that tabulate voting records on environmental issues are delighted to send you this information. Two of these are Consumer Federation of America, 1012 14th Street N.W., Washington, D.C. 20005; and The League of Conservation Voters, c/o Friends of the Earth, 917 15th Street N.W., Washington, D.C. 20005.

⊖ Write letters to legislators expressing your concern on pending bills, or propose needed legislation yourself. Lawmakers, particularly at the local level, are not used to receiving much mail, and 50 letters on an issue may seem like a landslide. Be sure to address your representative with proper title, full name, and correct spelling. Express your support or opposition on the issue in clear, concise terms. Include local editorials or clippings if they are pertinent. If you are not yet of legal voting age, do not mention this in your letter. You are, after all, a concerned citizen with a right to be heard. Keep a supply of postcards on hand for quick notes on immediate issues.

⊖ Join local, regional, or national groups that are lobbying for needed laws, bringing suits against polluters, and so on. Most of these organizations are not well financed and could use your help (*see* ORGANIZATIONS, page 111).

⊖ Be alert to attempts by developers and other special interest groups to sneak zoning changes and other variances through your governing body. Obtain schedules of hearings and open meetings from your city hall, county offices, and so on. Attend these hearings and meetings.

⊖ Testify at committee hearings, council meetings, supervisor and planning board hearings, and any others that may influence decisions on environmental questions. So few people are willing to voice their concerns at these meetings that your appearance may have a far greater effect than you expected.

⊖ Resort to the referendum if your best efforts have failed and a damaging law has been passed or an unsound zoning variance given. A good example of the use of the referendum on an environmental issue is one brought to a vote in Santa Barbara, Calif., in 1970. In June of that year, the Santa Barbara County Board of Supervisors granted a zoning variance to a developer despite protests from many individuals and groups. The variance allowed the creation of a housing development on land that was specifically designated ranching-recreation on the county's general plan. A petition calling on the supervisors to retract their decision or allow the voters to decide was circulated throughout the county. The required number of signatures was obtained to place the issue on the ballot, and on election day the voters of the county overturned the variance.

Obtaining a referendum requires many hours of volunteer effort and a thorough awareness of the legal requirements for wording of petitions, signatures, eligible signers, and so on. However, a successful referendum serves to remind officials that they are to administer the will of the people, rather than of special interests.

$\ominus$ Turn to the courts, as individuals or groups, for help in the environmental battle. Unfortunately, merely passing a law is no guarantee that it will be obeyed or enforced. Regulatory bodies such as the Atomic Energy Commission, National Air Pollution Control Administration, and others that should be looking out for our interests are often lax in this duty (48).

$\ominus$ If a regulatory body has not performed its function, suits may be filed against either the polluter or the neglectful governmental agency. There is considerable ambiguity regarding the rights of individuals or groups to sue either governmental agencies or polluters, but these matters are in the process of being clarified (48). For more up-to-date information, see

The Voter's Guide to Environmental Politics (BOOKS).

⊖ Bringing a case to court is a long, expensive business. Gather as much expertise as possible before bringing suit. Certain organizations may give advice and counsel in this area. Contact the Environmental Defense Fund, the Conservation Law Society, or the Sierra Club (*see* ORGANIZATIONS).

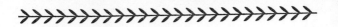

Population

We feel that many of the problems discussed in this guide are aggravated or created by the increased number of people occupying our earth, as well as by the wasteful habits of these people. As Pogo said, "We have met the enemy, and he is us." Pollution and other human problems are related both to the total number of people and to their uneven distribution. In the days before the arrival of the Pilgrims, the American continent had an average population density of 0.33 people per square mile. Now there are 55 people per square mile! (20). Although some areas of the country are virtually uninhabited, in other areas people are very densely packed.

Some feel that overpopulation is not as much of a worry for the United States as for, say, India. It is true that the growth rate of the United States is less than that of much of the world, but it is also true that Americans consume about half of the world's resources, while comprising only 6 percent of the world's population! (20). This makes our problem even more acute. Many estimate that we are closely approaching the sustained carrying capacity of our land (8). We will be hard put to supply enough food and essentials to the number of people that we ALREADY have. It appears that population control is a must.

In past times, large families were desired to in-

© 1970 Walt Kelly. Courtesy of Publishers-Hall Syndicate.

crease the family work force. Furthermore, having many children assured the father of being considered masculine. Now we are coming to realize that the world cannot afford families that produce more than two children. Each child in the United States, during his lifetime, will consume more than 56 million gallons of water, use 37 thousand gallons of gasoline, consume 5½ tons of meat, 9 tons of milk products, and 5½ tons of wheat (50). This consumption places a tremendous stress on our resources as

the number of people increases. Some feel that re-
placement (two children for two parents) should
be the goal, while others believe that we must have
fewer than two in order to reduce our population
to a workable size. At any rate, it is becoming clear
that unless we control our population size, increasingly crowded situations and growing frustrations
will explode in all sorts of violent and destructive
ways. Human beings have the intelligence to see far
enough into the future to predict disaster, but the
great question is whether they will apply this knowledge to their own lives.

Every nine seconds a baby is born in America (50).

ACTION

⊖ Support birth control programs at all levels. Education is the most important element if volun-
tary birth control is to be effective.

⊖ Inform yourself of the various birth control
methods available and of their effectiveness.
Using a device that is only 90 percent certain
is tantamount to asking for pregnancy. Planned
Parenthood and Zero Population Growth are
two organizations that will gladly inform ANY
PERSON, WITH NO OBLIGATION, of the
various types of birth control methods available. According to Ehrlich and Ehrlich (20),
the only techniques that are better than 95 percent sure to prevent pregnancy are the pill,

IUDs (intra-uterine devices), sterilization, abortion, and, yes, abstention. Not all of these may be suitable for you, but at least one of them should be. There isn't a couple in the world that shouldn't be using one of them!

⊖ Exercise your right as an individual to choose the form of birth control you feel suits you best. Be sufficiently informed yourself to determine if your gynecologist is prevented by personal or moral barriers from prescribing a form of contraception that you think desirable. If so, see another physician.

⊖ Work for abortion laws structured so as to allow each individual woman, with the advice of her physician, to decide whether she wishes an abortion to end an unwanted pregnancy.

⊖ Consider sterilization. The barriers to this procedure are now being broken down. It has been shown that sterilization in human beings results in neither obesity nor loss of sexual appetite (20). Vasectomy (a simple operation tying off the tubes containing the sperm) is very easy to obtain in most hospitals. Tubal ligation (a similar but more complex operation on the woman) is also easy to obtain. Check Ehrlich and Ehrlich (20) if you would like more detailed information.

⊖ Support sex education programs that stress the need for population control and teach birth control methods.

⊖ Eliminate the tax incentives for children. Allow no deduction for children, or certainly for no more than two. Perhaps families should be charged extra for children born after the first two.

⊖ Discuss the population problem with your friends on a personal level—it is everyman's problem, and it will be even more our children's problem.

⊖ Even if you can afford to support and educate several children, you should remember that there is a limit to the earth's capacity to provide, and that possibly the *world* cannot afford the extra children. Social pressures and pressure from relatives and friends should be ignored insofar as possible; we do not *owe* it to our parents to provide them with grandchildren!

⊖ Consider adoption as an alternative to producing your own. Children that already exist on this earth should be given every opportunity for a decent and meaningful life. If you have difficulty in adopting a child locally, write the Adoption Resource Exchange of North America, 44 E. 23rd Street, New York, N.Y. 10010, for help and information.

Will Technology Save Us?

Many of us are content to view the environmental crisis complacently, trusting that technology will save us without our stirring from in front of our TV sets. However, we are forgetting that undirected technology can become a monster, and that in fact it is a chief cause of our present ecological problems. Furthermore, there's only so much that technology can do to save a world that is already populated beyond its capacity to provide, with no end yet in sight to our population explosion.

Technology can be a useful and important tool in our fight for environmental quality. However, we the people create the social and political climate that influences the goals of our technology. Our efforts to attain environmental health and abundant life in accord with all of nature must begin within ourselves.

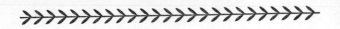

Recommended Information and Action Sources

Books

Abbey, E. 1968. *Desert Solitaire: A Season in the Wilderness.* New York: McGraw-Hill, $5.95. *Deeply felt memoir by a park ranger who loves the high desert and fought to preserve it.*

American Association of University Women. 1970. *If You Want to Save Your Environment . . . Start at Home.* Palo Alto: Peninsula Press, Inc., 75¢.

American Chemical Society. 1969. *Cleaning Our Environment: The Chemical Basis for Action.* Washington, D.C.: American Chemical Society, $2.75. *Fairly detailed accounts of air, water, and land pollution, with an abundance of facts.*

Ardrey, R. 1968. *The Territorial Imperative.* New York: Delta-Dell, $2.95.

Bates, M. 1960. *The Forest and the Sea: A Look at the Economy of Nature and the Ecology of Man.* New York: Random House, $1.65.

Carson, R. 1962. *Silent Spring.* New York: Crest, 95¢. *The classic.*

Committee on Government Operations. 1970. *Phosphates in Detergents and the Eutrophication of America's Water.* Washington, D.C.: U.S. Government Printing

Office, 40¢. *A subcommittee turns on; thorough analysis of the problem.*

Committee on Resources and Man. 1969. *Resources and Man.* San Francisco: W. H. Freeman and Company, $2.95. *An informative book organized with resources as topics.*

Commoner, B. 1966. *Science and Survival.* New York: Viking, $1.65.

Conservation Foundation, The. 1970. *Your Right to Clean Air.* Washington, D.C.: The Conservation Foundation. Free. *A manual for citizen action.*

Council on Environmental Quality. 1970. *Environmental Quality.* Washington, D.C.: U.S. Government Printing Office, $1.75. *Facts of figures detailing the problems thoroughly.*

Cox, G. (editor). 1969. *Readings in Conservation Ecology.* New York: Appleton, $4.95.

Curtis, R., and E. Hogan. 1969. *Perils of the Peaceful Atom.* New York: Ballantine, $1.25. *Discusses problems of nuclear power generation.*

Darnay, A., and W. E. Franklin. 1969. *The Role of Packaging in Solid Waste Management 1966 to 1976.* Washington, D.C.: U.S. Government Printing Office, $2.25. *Excellent work describing environmental aspects of overpackaging.*

Dasmann, R. 1965. *The Destruction of California.* New York: Macmillan, $1.50. *Excellent case history; not just for Californians.*

Davis, Adelle. 1970 rev. *Let's Cook It Right.* Signet, $1.50.

DeBell, G. (editor). 1970. *The Environmental Handbook.* New York: Friends of the Earth–Ballantine, 95¢.

DeBell, G. (editor). 1970. *The Voter's Guide to Environmental Politics.* New York: Friends of the Earth–Ballantine, 95¢.

Ehrlich, P. 1968. *The Population Bomb.* New York: Ballantine, 95¢. *Impressive, frightening forecast.*

Ehrlich, P., and A. H. Ehrlich. 1970. *Population, Re-*

sources, Environment. San Francisco: W. H. Freeman and Company, $8.95. *Well-documented, thorough, informative references.*

Environmental Action. 1970. *Earth Day—The Beginning.* New York: Bantam, $1.25.

Galbraith, J. K. 1969. *The Affluent Society.* New York: Mentor, 95¢.

———. 1969. *The New Industrial State.* Boston: Houghton Mifflin, $6.95.

Goldstein, J. 1969. *Garbage As You Like It.* Emmaus, Pa.: Rodale Books.

Graham, F., Jr. 1970. *Since Silent Spring.* Boston: Houghton Mifflin, $6.95. *Takes up where* Silent Spring *left off and relates the story of Rachel Carson.*

Guttmacher, A. F. 1964. *The Complete Book of Birth Control.* New York: Ballantine, 95¢.

Hardin, G. (editor). 1969. *Population, Evolution, and Birth Control.* San Francisco: W. H. Freeman and Company, $6.00.

Hunter, B. 1964. *Gardening Without Poisons.* Boston: Houghton Mifflin, $5.00.

King, T. 1953. *Water: Miracle of Nature.* New York: Collier Books, 95¢.

Laycock, G. 1970. *The Diligent Destroyers.* Garden City, N.Y.: Doubleday and Company, Inc. *A critical look at the industries and agencies that are permanently defacing the American landscape.*

Leopold, A. 1966. *A Sand County Almanac.* New York: Oxford University Press, $1.95.

McHarg, I. 1969. *Design with Nature.* Garden City, N.Y.: Natural History Press, $19.95. *Environmental approach to regional and community planning.*

Mackenthun, K. M. 1969. *The Practice of Water Pollution Biology.* Washington, D.C.: U.S. Government Printing Office, $1.50. *An excellent technical description of water pollution.*

Marine, G. 1969. *America the Raped.* New York: Simon and Schuster, $5.95.

Marx, W. 1969. *The Frail Ocean.* New York: Ballantine, 95¢. *Easily read book on marine pollution.*

Mitchell, J. G., and C. L. Stallings (editors). 1970. *Ecotactics: The Sierra Club Handbook for Environmental Activists.* New York: Pocket Books, 95¢.

Morris, D. 1969. *The Naked Ape.* New York: Dell, 95¢. *Places man in perspective as a member of the animal kingdom.*

National Wildlife Federation, 1970. *Conservation Directory.* Washington, D.C.: National Wildlife Federation, $1.50. *A listing of organizations, agencies, and officials concerned with natural resource use and management.*

Osborn, F. 1949. *Our Plundered Planet.* Boston: Little, Brown, $1.95.

Rienow, R., and L. Rienow. 1969. *Moment in the Sun.* New York: Ballantine, 95¢. *Easily read book; the air pollution portion is particularly good.*

Rodale, J. (editor). 1969. *The Complete Book of Gardening.* Emmaus, Pa.: Rodale Press, $8.95.

——— (editor). 1969. *Encyclopedia of Organic Gardening.* Emmaus, Pa.: Rodale Press, $9.95.

——— *How to Grow Vegetables and Fruits by the Organic Method.* Emmaus, Pa.: Rodale Press, $9.95.

Russell, J., and P. Russell. 1969. *On the Loose.* New York: Sierra Club–Ballantine, $3.95. *Two young men wander the West; prose and poetry.*

Sears, P. B. 1970. *The Living Landscape.* New York: Basic Books, $4.95.

Shepard, P., and D. McKinley (editors). 1968. *The Subversive Science.* Boston: Houghton Mifflin, $5.95. *A humanities-oriented, interdisciplinary approach to the population problem.*

Shurcliff, William A. 1970. *SST and Sonic Boom Handbook.* New York: Friends of the Earth–Ballantine, 95¢.

Swatek, Paul. 1970. *The User's Guide to the Protection of the Environment.* New York: Friends of the Earth–Ballantine, 312 pages, $1.25.

Terry, Mark. 1971. *Teaching for Survival*. New York: Friends of the Earth-Ballantine, 213 pages, $1.25.

Thoreau, H. 1854. *Walden*. New York: Mentor, 50¢. *I get by without the help of my friends.*

Turner, J. S. 1970. *The Chemical Feast*. New York: Grossman, 95¢.

United States Department of the Interior. 1968. *Man— An Endangered Species?* Washington, D.C.: U.S. Government Printing Office, $1.50. *Picture book on population problem. Lightweight but well illustrated.*

United States Government Publications. Send for *Price Lists by Topics* to the Superintendent of Documents, U.S. Government Printing Office, Washington, D.C. 20402.

Whiteside, T. 1970. *Defoliation*. New York: Ballantine, 95¢. *Discusses some of the ecological effects.*

Whyte, W. H. 1970. *The Last Landscape*. Garden City, N.Y.: Anchor, $1.95.

Periodicals

Audubon. Bimonthly; $8.50 per year; 1130 Fifth Avenue, New York, N.Y. 10028.

Compost Science, The Journal of Waste Recycling. Bimonthly; $6.00 per year; Rodale Press, 33 E. Minor Street, Emmaus, Pa., 18049.

Cry California. Membership: quarterly; $9.00 a year; California Tomorrow, Monadnock Building, 681 Market Street, San Francisco, Calif. 94105.

Environment. Ten copies per year (Jan.–Feb., July– Aug. are combined); $8.50 per year; P.O. Box 755, Bridgeton, Mo. 63044.

Environment Action Bulletin. Weekly; $10.00 per year; Rodale Press, Emmaus, Pa., 18049.

Environmental Science and Technology. Monthly; $5.00 a year for members, $7.00 for nonmembers; 1155 16th Street N.W., Washington, D.C. 20036.

Environmental Quality Magazine. Four EQM a year and

14 Newsletters; $6.50 per year now, $10.70 later; Environmental Awareness Associates, 6355 Topanga Canyon, Suite 327, Woodland Hills, Calif. 91364.

Living Wilderness. Quarterly membership; Wilderness Society, 729 15th Street N.W., Washington, D.C. 20005.

National Wildlife. Bimonthly, membership; $5.00 per year; National Wildlife-Federation, 381 West Center Street, Marion, Ohio 43302.

Oceans. Bimonthly; $12.00 per year; 1150 Anchorage Lane, San Diego, Calif. 92106.

Organic Gardening and Farming. Monthly; $5.85 per year; 33 E. Minor Street, Rodale Press, Emmaus, Pa. 18049.

Ranger Ricks Nature Magazine. Ten a year, $6.00 per year, National Wild Life Federation, 381 West Center Street, Marion, Ohio 43302.

Science News. Monthly; $7.50 per year; 231 West Center Street, Marion, Ohio 43302.

Sierra Club Bulletin. Monthly; member's cost with dues $12.00, non-member $5.00 per year; 1050 Mills Tower, San Francisco, Calif. 94104.

Sunset Magazine. Monthly; $5.00 per year, Menlo Park, Calif. 94025.

Whole Earth Catalog. Fall and Spring Issues plus 4 supplements; $8.00 per year; Basic volume $3.00; Portola Institute, 558 Santa Cruz, Menlo Park, Calif. 94025.

Organizations

American Forestry Association. 919 17th Street N.W., Washington, D.C. 20006. *Promotes conservation of forests and allied resources.*

Citizens for Clean Air. 40 W. 57th Street, New York, N.Y. 10019.

Citizens Committee on Natural Resources. 1346 Connecticut Avenue N.W., Washington, D.C. 20036. *Lobby for conservation issues.*

Citizens League Against the Sonic Boom. 19 Appleton Street, Cambridge, Mass. 02138.

Concern, Incorporated. P.O. Box 19287, Washington, D.C. 20036.

Conservation Associates. 1500 Mills Tower, 200 Bush Street, San Francisco, Calif. 94104. *Provides assistance in land planning and acquisition to conservationists.*

Conservation Education Association. 1250 Connecticut Avenue N.W., Washington, D.C. 20036. *Encourages conservation education programs, provides literature.*

Conservation Foundation. 1250 Connecticut Avenue N.W., Washington, D.C. 20036 *Research, education, and information on conservation topics. Privately supported.*

Conservation Law Society of America. Mills Tower, 220 Bush Street, San Francisco, Calif. 94104. *Counsels litigants in cases of national importance on a fee basis.*

Consumers Education and Protective Association. 6048 Ogontoy Avenue, Philadelphia, Pa. 19141.

Defenders of Wildlife. 1346 Connecticut Avenue N.W., Washington, D.C. 20036

Ducks, Unlimited. P.O. Box 66300, Chicago, Ill. 60666. *Works to conserve wild waterfowl habitats in U.S. and Canada.*

Ecology Action. P.O. Box 9334, Berkeley, Calif. 94709.

Environmental Action, Inc. 2000 P Street N.W., Washington, D.C. 20036.

Environmental Defense Fund, Inc. P.O. Box 740, Stony Brook, N.Y. 11790. *Nonprofit organization. A leader in environmental court cases.*

Friends of the Earth. 30 E. 42nd Street, New York, N.Y. 10017. *Aggressive, international conservation organization.*

Garden Clubs of America. 598 Madison Avenue, New York, N.Y. 10022.

International Union for the Conservation of Nature and Natural Resources. 1110 Morges, Geneva, Switzerland. *Besides gardening instruction, provides informa-*

tion on pending legislation.

Izaak Walton League of America. 1326 Waukegan Road, Glenview, Ill. 60025. *Conservation education on many fronts.*

John Muir Institute for Environmental Studies. 451 Pacific Avenue, San Francisco, Calif. 94133.

League of Women Voters Education Fund. 1730 M Street N.W., Washington, D.C. 20036. *Publishes well-reasoned stands on public issues.*

National Association of Soil and Water Conservation Districts. 1025 Vermont Avenue N.W., Washington, D.C. 20005.

National Audubon Society. 1130 Fifth Avenue, New York, N.Y. 10038. *Very vigorous group in conservation efforts of all sorts, not just little old ladies in tennis shoes.*

National Council of State Garden Clubs, Inc. 4401 Magnolia Avenue, St. Louis, Mo. 63110.

National Parks Association. 1701 18th Street N.W., Washington, D.C. 20009.

National Wildlife Federation. 1412 16th Street N.W., Washington, D.C. 20036. *Informative, aware, and active. A standout organization. Publishes the* Conservation Directory.

Nature Conservancy, The. 1522 K Street N.W., Washington, D.C. 20005. *Acquires threatened lands for scientific and educational purposes. Nonprofit.*

North American Wildlife Foundation. 709 Wire Building, Washington, D.C. 20005. *Sponsors research in wildlife and other aspects of natural resource conservation.*

Open Space Institute. 145 East 52nd Street, New York, N.Y. 10022. *Professional consultants in preservation of open spaces.*

Planned Parenthood. 515 Madison Avenue, New York, N.Y. 10022. *Provides information and aids in nonparenthood, too.*

Rachel Carson Trust for the Living Environment, Inc.

8940 Jones Mill Road, Washington, D.C. 20015. *Serves as clearinghouse of information on environmental contamination and ecology in general.*

Resources for the Future, Inc. 1145 19th Street N.W., Washington, D.C. 20006. *Source of natural resource statistics.*

Scientist's Institute for Public Information. 30 W. 68th Street, New York, N.Y. 10021. *Provides public with scientific information on environmental problems.*

Sierra Club. 1050 Mills Tower, San Francisco, Calif. 94104. *The foremost of the fighters.*

Sport Fishing Institute. 719 13th Street N.W., Washington, D.C. 20005.

Trout Unlimited. 2526 State Street, P.O. Box 1807, Saginaw, Mich. 48605. *Supports high standards of water quality.*

Urban America. 1717 Massachusetts Avenue N.W., Washington, D.C. 20036.

Water Pollution Control Federation. 3900 Wisconsin Avenue N.W., Washington, D.C. 20016.

Wilderness Society, The. 729 15th Street N.W., Washington, D.C. 20005. *Defends and increases knowledge of wilderness.*

Zero Population Growth. 367 State Street, Los Altos, Calif. 94022. *Grass roots population control movement.*

Literature Cited

1. Stockton, Bill. 1970. "Refuse Crisis in U.S. Grows by Truckloads." *Los Angeles Times*, November 26.
2. Train, Russell E., R. Cahn, and G. MacDonald. 1970. *Environmental Quality*. U.S. Government Printing Office, Washington, D.C.
3. Reynolds Aluminum Advertisement. 1970. *Time* Magazine, February 16.
4. Adolph Coors Company Press Release. June 19, 1970.
5. Anonymous. 1970. "The Return of the Returnables?" *Newsweek*, September 28, 1970.
6. Darnay, Arsen, and W. E. Franklin. 1969. *The Role of Packaging in Solid Waste Management 1966–1976*. U.S. Department of Health, Education, and Welfare. U.S. Government Printing Office, Washington, D.C.
7. American Chemical Society. 1969. *Cleaning Our Environment; The Chemical Basis for Action*. Washington, D.C.
8. Cloud, Preston (editor). 1969. *Resources and Man*. W. H. Freeman and Company, San Francisco.
9. Anon. 1970. "Milk Bottles to Tiles." *Chem. and Eng. News*, 48(35):11 (August 24, 1970).
10. Dasmann, Raymond F. 1969. *The Destruction of California*. Collier Books (Macmillan), New York.
11. *Los Angeles Times*. May 8, 1970.
12. Goldstein, Jerome. 1970. "Recycle Paper and Save the Dump." *Compost Science* 11(3):4–7 (May–June 1970).
13. Anon. 1970. "A New Market and Methodology." *Compost Science* 11(3): 7 (May–June 1970).

14. Manheim, F. T., R. H. Meade, and G. Bond. 1970. "Suspended Matter in Surface Waters of the Atlantic Continental Margin from Cape Cod to the Florida Keys." *Science* 167(3917):371–76.
15. Benglesdorf, Irving. 1970. "Power Plants Not Without Problems." *Los Angeles Times,* February 24.
16. Southern California Edison Company, personal communication.
17. Department of State Publication 8510. 1970. *Problems of Population Growth. General Foreign Policy 241.*
18. Jaeger, R. J., and R. J. Rubin. 1970. "Plasticizers from Plastic Devices: Extraction, Metabolism, and Accumulation by Biological Systems." *Science* 170: 400–402.
19. Fradkan, Philip. 1970. "Huge Power Plants Pose Threat to Desert Environment." *Los Angeles Times,* October 18.
20. Ehrlich, P., and A. Ehrlich. 1970. *Population, Resources and Environment.* W. H. Freeman and Company, San Francisco.
21. *Ecology Begins at Home.* 1970. Pamphlet compiled by the Conservation Ecology Action Group, San Fernando Valley State College.
22. Rodale, J. E. (editor). 1959. *Encyclopedia of Organic Gardening.* Rodale Books, Inc., Emmaus, Pa. (1145 pages).
23. Abelson, P. 1970. "Methyl Mercury." *Science* 169 (3942):237.
24. Cohn, Victor. 1970. "U.S. Waking Up to Growing Danger of Mercury Pollution." *Los Angeles Times,* July 27.
25. Chow, R. J., and M. S. Johnstone. 1965. "Pb Isotopes in Gasoline and Aerosols of the Los Angeles Basin." *Science* 147:502.
26. Gilliam, Jerry. 1970. "Assembly OKs Bill to Take Lead Out of Gasoline by 1977." *Los Angeles Times,* July 23.

27. Cohn, Victor. 1970. "Lead in Air Threatens San Diego, Study Finds." *Los Angeles Times,* August 8.

28. Anon. 1970. "Lead Content in Air Reported Increasing." *Santa Barbara News Press,* August 7.

29. Dawson, William (chairman). 1970. *Phosphates in Detergents and the Eutrophication of America's Waters.* 23rd Report by the Committee on Government Operations. U.S. Government Printing Office, Washington, D.C.

30. Anon. 1970. "Mink Yes, Tiger No." *Time Magazine,* August 31.

31. Epstein, Samuel S. 1970. "NTA." *Environment* 12 (7):2–11 (September 1970).

32. Anon. 1970. "Pollution: Softer Soap?" *Newsweek,* August 24.

33. Mrak, Emil M. (chairman). 1969. *Report of the Secretary's Commission on Pesticides and Their Relationship to Environmental Health.* Parts 1 and 2. U.S. Department of Health, Education, and Welfare. U.S. Government Printing Office, Washington, D.C.

34. Stecher, Paul G. (editor). 1968. *The Merck Index: An Encyclopedia of Chemicals and Drugs.* Merck and Co., Inc., Rahway, N.J. (1713 pages).

35. Benglesdorf, Irving S. 1970. "Nerve Gas Isn't Really Gas—But It's As Deadly As Reported." *Los Angeles Times,* August 8.

36. Nelson, Harry. 1970. "FDA to Indicate Doubt of Pest Strip's Safety." *Los Angeles Times,* August 4, 1970.

37. van den Bosch, Robert. 1970. *Prescribing for the Environment in Pesticides* (Dahlstenn et al., editors). Scientists Institute for Public Information, 30 E. 68th Street, New York, N.Y.

38. Shea, Kevin P. 1969. "Name Your Poison." *Environment* 11(7):30 (September 1969).

39. Turner, I. S. 1970. *The Chemical Feast*. Grossman, New York.

40. Hager, Philip. 1970. "The End of a California Dream?" *Los Angeles Times*, July 31.

41. MacIntyre, Ferren J. Personal communication. Address: Department of Biological Sciences, University of California at Santa Barbara.

42. Ottinger, Betty A. 1970. *What Every Woman Should Know—And Do—About Pollution*. EP Press, New York (94 pages).

43. W.P.C.F. Standards Methods Committee, Subcommittee on Biodegradability. 1967. "Required Characteristics and Measurement of Biodegradability." *J.W.P.C.F.* (*Journal Water Pollution Control Federation*.) 39(7):1232–35.

45. Gruchow, Nancy. 1970. "Detergents: Side Effects of the Washday Miracles." *Science* 167 (3915): 151.

46. Anon. 1970. "Strong Complaints Lodged by Enzyme Detergent Users." *Los Angeles Times*, October 21.

47. Angino, E. E., et al. 1970. "Arsenic in Detergents: Possible Danger and Pollution Hazard." *Science* 168 (3929):389–90.

48. Gilluly, Richard. 1970. "Taking Polluters to the Courts." *Science News* 98:273–74 (September 26, 1970).

49. *Compost Science*. 1970. 11(3).

50. Young, Gordon, and J. P. Blair. 1970. "Pollution: Threat to Man's Only House." *National Geographic* 138(6):738–81 (December 1970).

51. Laycock, George. 1970. *The Diligent Destroyers*. Doubleday and Company, Inc., Garden City, N.Y.

52. Wakefield, L. H. 1969. Goleta Slough. *Audubon Magazine* 71:154–55.

53. Swatek, Paul. 1970. *The User's Guide to the Protection of the Environment*. Friends of the Earth–Ballantine, New York.

54. Whiteside, T. 1970. *Defoliation*. Friends of the Earth–Ballantine, New York.
55. Eisenbud, M. 1970. "Environmental Protection in the City of New York." *Science* **170**:706–12.

Some Suggested Key Index Words

abortion 103
adoption 104
advertising 28, 45
air pollution 37–39, 41–45
aluminum 8–10, 52
aluminum cans 7, 35
appliances 2
arsenic 79
autos 2, 36–39, 41–45
baby food 12
baby food jars 12, 28
bags, paper 18–19
bags, plastic 15–16
beer 11
bicycles 36–37
billboards 69
biodegradability 87–89
birth control 102–104
blenders 2
books 25
bottles 2, 10–13
cans 2, 35
cardboard 30
cards 26
carpools 37
Christmas 21, 27, 72
cleansers 85–92
clothes washer, dryer 40
compost 35, 45, 57, 59–60
consumer action 7, 70–72
consumption 1
containers 7–19
DDT 81
DDVP 76, 84
detergents 14, 85–92
developments 67–69
diapers 30
dishwasher 40, 90
dogfood 8
doggie bags 56
dryers 2
education 5, 103
egg containers 28
electrical power 39–41
electrical appliances 2, 39–41
endangered wildlife 61–64
enzymes 86, 91
estuaries 67
eutrophication 85–92
fertilizer 57, 61

firewood 21
flea collars 76, 84
food 17, 53–57
food additives 53–54
furs 63
garden 47, 55, 73–85
general plan 67–69
glasphalt 10
Glass Container Manufacturers
    Institute 12
glass recycling 7, 10–13, 17
herbicides 84–85
holidays 72
industry 42
insecticides 73–84
introduction 1
IUD 103
jars 11–12
jewelry 53
kitchen drippings 17, 57
landuse 31, 64–69
lead 92–94
left-overs 17
letters 26
light bulbs 40–41
magazine 24
mercury 94–95
metallic toxins 92–95
metals 52–53
milk containers 17
mulching 85
newspaper 21–24, 35
"no-pest" strips 76, 84
NTA 86–87
packaging 7
paper 2, 7, 18–31
    plates 30
    towels 28–30
pens 13, 16
pesticides 73–85
    acceptable 82–83
petroleum products 36–41,
    92–94
phosphates 86–92
plastics 2, 7, 14–16, 28
    bags 15–16
    bottle 15
    silverware 16
Pill 102–103
political action 96–99

pollutants 73–95
population 5, 100–104
power generation 39, 42
progress 5
PVC 14
recycling 5, 7–12, 23–24, 30–36,
  49–52
recycling centers 31–36
recycling symbol 33
refrigerators 2
resources to be conserved 7
rules to live by 4–6
scrap metal dealer 9
seed treatment 94–95
sewage treatment 16, 48–52, 57,
  61, 91
showers 46
soaps 57–58, 85–91
solid waste 1, 24, 30–36
stationery 26
sterilization 103
styrofoam 16, 28

tampons 16
telephone books 24
television sets 2
timber 19–21
tin (cans) 7
tires 2
toasters 2, 47
toilet 30
toilet paper 28–30
toys 16, 94
trading stamps 71
transportation 36–39, 42, 66–67
trees 18, 23
washing machines 2
water 45–52, 48–52, 94–95
wax-cardboard containers 17
whales 63–64
wine 11
wood 19–21
wrapping 26
zoning 67–69